Chemistry for High School

Chemistry for High School

First Edition, 2019

Email: support@elementalscience.com

ISBN # 978-1-935614-68-5

Printed in the USA for worldwide distribution

For more copies write to:
Elemental Science
PO Box 79
Niceville, FL 32588
support@elementalscience.com

Copyright Policy

Chemistry for High School Table of Contents

Unit 2: Bonding and Reactions

Unit 3: Water and Equilibrium

Unit 4: Organic Chemistry and More

Appendix

Introduction to this Guide

Welcome to Chemistry! This year, you will learn about matter, atomic structure, reactions, and much more. In this guide, you will find three types of schedules, as well as notes with the assignments for each week. To get links to the textbook, teacher guide, experiment, and quick-links for the activities in this guide, please visit:

💻 https://elementalscience.com/blogs/resources/chs

Three Courses in One

This guide contains the plans for three courses in one book. These are:

- **Honors** - The plans in this option are for a lab science, 1-credit *Honors Chemistry* course. There are textbook assignments, experiments, events in science, optional hands-on activities, and written work with these plans. Expect to take about 5 to 6 hours a week to complete these plans. We recommend this option for students who plan on going into the sciences. The honors course will also fulfill a lab science credit for graduation.
- **Standard** - The plans in this option are for a standard lab science, 1-credit *High School Chemistry* course. There are textbook assignments, experiments or online labs, and written work with these plans. Expect to take about 4 to 5 hours a week to complete these plans. We recommend this option for students who are not and for students who are planning on going into the sciences. The standard course will fulfill a lab science credit for graduation.
- **Survey** - The plans in this option are for an information-only, 1-credit *Survey of Chemistry* course. There are textbook assignments, written work, and events in science with these plans. There are no experiments or hands-on activities scheduled with these plans. Expect to take about 4 to 5 hours a week to complete these plans. We recommend this option for students who are not planning on going into the sciences and do not need a lab science credit for graduation.

Each of the scheduling pages will note at the top which course the plans are for. These schedules for these courses are suggestions; please check wil your local oversight contact to make sure that you are meeting your state's graduation requirements. Please feel free to tailor this program to the needs of your students.

An Explanation of the Sections

After the scheduling pages, you will find the notes sheets. These sheets are divided into four sections - textbook, experiments, events in science, and hands-on activities. Here is an explanation of each of these sections.

Textbook

For this study, we have chosen to use the standard text book, *CK-12 Chemistry Intermediate.*

You can download this text as a pdf from the resource page above. You will complete the reading assignment and then answer several of the questions from the text. These answers should be added to the reading section of the science notebooks. You will also define several of the key terms from the chapter. The definitions should be added to the glossary section of the science notebook.

Experiment

All the experiments come from the *Standard Home School Chemistry Laboratory Kit Instruction Manual*, along with the corresponding experiment kit. You can download the guide for free and purchase the kit (CK01B Standard Home School Chemistry Laboratory Kit) from here:

💻 https://www.thehomescientist.com/ck01b-main.php

With each of these experiments, you will find a purpose, required pre-reading, procedure, lab notebook assignments, and lab questions. For each week, we have included a supply list for your convenience. If you would like to see a full list of the household supplies you will need in addition to the experiment kit, please see pg. 239 in the Appendix.

We have also incorporated an optional online lab into the standard course. These online labs are available through Beyond Labz. You can visit the resource page for this program for directions on how to sign up and use these labs or visit their website directly at:

💻 https://www.beyondlabz.com/

As part of unit 1, the standard- and honors-course students will complete a full lab report for one of the experiments. We have included an explanation of what a full lab report includes after this introduction.

Events in Science

This section gives two options for the Events in Science section. One will familiarize you with current events in science, as you research on the internet for the various topics. The other will familiarize you with the key historical figures in chemistry through the scientist biography report. We have included two articles to explain these options in more depth following this introduction.

Hands-on Activities

We have also included optional hands-on experiments for each week. You can see a list of the supplies you will need for these in the Appendix on pg. 241.

The Science Notebook

This year, you will each create a science notebook. Each notebook should contain the following sections:

- 🕮 Reading (All Students) - This section of the notebook will contain any notes you have taken, along with the answers to the questions that were assigned each week.
- 🕮 Lab (Standard- and Honors-Course Students Only) - This section of the notebook will house the notes from the experiments you have done, along with any other materials relating to the labs.
- 🕮 Events (Survey- and Honors-Course Students Only) - This section of the notebook will include either the current events article summaries or the historical reports you have done.
- 🕮 Glossary (All Students) - This section of the notebook will have the definitions for the assigned vocabulary words.

This notebook can be a composition book, divided into the required sections, or a three-ring binder with dividers for each section.

Grading and Credits

The three options in this guide meet the requirements for a full credit of high school chemistry, as explained above. Each week, the student will answer lab and textbook questions, do events in science written work, and define vocabulary that can count toward a classwork grade for the course. The textbook for this course has chapter tests available for free in the quizzes and tests packet. We suggest that you use these for the exam grade for the course. We suggest you use the following percentages to come up with a final grade for the course:

- ☞ Class work: 70%
- ☞ Exam: 30%

Note - A grading rubric for the Scientist Biography Reports can be found on pg. 243 in the Appendix.

Students Going Into The Sciences

If your students plan to go on to major in the sciences, we suggest that you also add an in-depth project and a research report at some point during the year to this program. An explanation of the in-depth project and of the research report can be found on the following pages.

Final Thoughts

As the authors and publishers of this curriculum, we encourage you to contact us with any questions or problems that you might have concerning *Chemistry for High School* at support@elementalscience.com. We will be more than happy to answer you as soon as we are able. We trust that you and your students will enjoy *Chemistry for High School*!

What a full Lab Report should include

It is very important that all students begin to understand the process of writing scientific laboratory reports. Learning technical writing is a skill that must be practiced in order to become proficient. Having your students write laboratory reports also helps them to think critically as they analyzes the data that they have observed in the experiments. It will also give them a good basis for scientific writing that will help to prepare them for college level work.

The Components

Although there are some variations to a scientific lab report depending on the discipline you are writing for, they all contain the same basic components. Below is a general outline of the components of a scientific lab report:

1. Title
2. Abstract
3. Introduction
4. Materials and Procedure
5. Results (includes observations and data)
6. Conclusion
7. Works Cited

Each section of the scientific lab report should include specific information. The following is an explanation of what each section should have.

Title

This section should summarize the scientific experiment in 10 words or less and use key words in the report.

Abstract

An abstract gives a one paragraph synopsis of the research that the scientist has done. Generally, the scientist will write a full research report and the abstract can let the reader know if reading the full report would be beneficial. The abstract should contain the data and conclusions of the report in two hundred words or less. If you have not completed an associated research report, you can use this to summarize their research.

Introduction

The introduction section of the report is designed to give the reader the basis for the report, the reason why it was completed, and the background about what is already known about the experiment. Usually this section answers, "Why did we do this study?", "What information was known before we began the experiment?", and "What is the purpose of the study?"

Materials and Procedures

This section tells the reader what specific equipment and supplies were used in the experiment. You will also need to describe how the equipment and supplies were used. It is also important to describe when and where the experiment was conducted. The purpose of this information is to allow any person that reads the scientific report to be able to replicate the results. Without being able to replicate the results, the data obtained are not confirmable.

Results

The main purpose of the results section is to present the data that were obtained during the experiment. It is important that you present just the data and avoid analyzing or making conclusions about the data, as there is another section for this. The results section is also the place to include tables, graphs, and data tables. These should be easily understood by the average reader and be well labeled.

Conclusion

In the conclusion section you should focus on analyzing the data. Don't just reiterate the data; rather, draw conclusions from the data. It is permissible to draw speculative conclusions; just remember to state that is what you are doing. In this section, you should also discuss if the hypothesis was confirmed or invalidated and if further experimentation should be carried out to refine your hypothesis. You must also discuss any errors that occurred during the lab; these are usually not human errors but rather systematic errors that occur while conducting the experiment. Systematic errors can be caused by improper calibration of equipment, changes in the environment, and estimation errors. In the conclusion, it is important to present these errors that may have occurred in your experiment. This section is usually written in third person, passive, past tense.

Works Cited

This is the listing of the research materials used in the report to give background or to help corroborate the data. All outside sources must be cited. The format you will use for the works cited (i.e., MLA, APA, Turabian etc.) will depend upon the scientific field that this lab report relates to.

The Style

When formatting the lab reports, there are some basic guidelines about style that you should know.

1. Have a one inch margin and use 12pt New Times Roman font.

2. All chemical formulas should be formatted properly (i.e. Cl_2, H_2O)
3. Chemical structures that are drawn should be neat and easily readable.
4. Pay attention to formatting, spelling, and the overall look of the lab report.

More Information on Lab Reports

We recommend two books for your student to better prepare for writing scientific papers and lab reports. These books cover in greater detail what we covered in the previous section and they can be easily obtained from Amazon or your university library.

- *A Student Handbook For Writing In Biology* by Karin Kinsely
- *Making Sense: Life Sciences: A Student's Guide to Research and Writing* by Margot Northey

Adding Current Events into your Science Studies

Step 1 - Choose the article.

The first step is to choose an appropriate article. Usually, I try to pick one from the field of science that we are studying. You can subscribe to a kid's science magazine, do a Google search, or check out our Science News for Students to find possible articles. Once you have collected a list of options, peruse through them and pick one that you think will interest your student.

Step 2 - Read the article.

The next step is to have the students read the actual article. Simply hand them the article and tell each of them to come see you when they are done reading it.

Step 3 - Discuss the article.

The third step is to discuss the article the student is reading. I typically ask questions like:

- What was the article about?
- What do you think about (a piece of research or an experiment that the article pointed out)?
- How does the article relate to (something that we have studied on the subject)?
- Did you find the article to be interesting?
- Do you agree with the opinion(s) stated in the article?

Step 4 - Write a summary.

The final step to adding current events to your science students is to have each student write a summary. Once you finish the discussion, ask your students to write three to five sentences on the article, including their opinion on it. Since you have already talked about the piece, this step is easy for the students to do.

The Scientist Biography Report

Step 1 - Research

Begin by looking for a biography on the scientist at the library. Then, look for articles on the chemist in magazines, newspapers, encyclopedias, or on the Internet. You will need to know the following about your scientist to write your report:

- 🕮 Biographical information on the scientist (i.e., where they were born, their parents, siblings, and how they grew up);
- 🕮 The scientist's education (i.e., where they went to school, what kind of student they were, what they studied, and so on);
- 🕮 Their scientific contributions (i.e., research that they participated in, any significant discoveries they made, and the state of the world at the time of their contributions).

As you read over the material you have gathered, be sure to write down any facts you glean in your own words. You can do this on the sheet below or on separate index cards. You can read more about this method by clicking below:

💻 http://elementalblogging.com/the-index-card-system/

Step 2 - Create an Outline

Now that your research is completed, you are ready to begin the process of writing a report on your chosen scientist. You are going to organize the notes you took during step two into a formal outline, which you will use next week to write the rough draft of your report. Use the outline template provided on the student sheets as a guide. You should include information on why you chose the particular scientist in your introduction section. For the conclusion section of the outline, you need to include why you believe someone else should learn about your chosen scientist and your impression of the scientist (i.e., Did you like the scientist? Do you feel that they made a significant impact on the field of chemistry?).

The outline you create can look like the one below:

Scientist Biography Outline

I. Introduction & Biological Information on the Scientist (4-6 points)

II. The Scientist's Education (4-6 points)

III. The Scientist's Contributions (1-3 sub categories each with 4-5 points)

IV. Conclusion (4-5 points)

Step 3 - Write a Rough Draft

In the last step, you created a formal outline for your scientist biography report; now, it is time to take that outline and turn it into a rough draft. Simply take the points on your outline, combine them, and add in sentence openers to create a cohesive paragraph. Here's what your rough draft should look like:

- 🕮 Paragraph 1 (from outline point I): introduce the scientist;
- 🕮 Paragraph 2 (from outline point II): tell about the scientist's education;
- 🕮 Paragraph 3-5 (from outline point III): share the scientist's contributions (one paragraph for each contribution);
- 🕮 Paragraph 6 (from outline point IV): share your thoughts on the scientist and why someone should learn about him or her.

You can choose to hand write or type up your rough draft on a separate sheet of paper. However, keep in mind that you will need a typed version for the final step.

Step 5- Revise to Create a Final Draft

Now that you have a typed, double-spaced rough draft, look over it one more time to make any changes you would like. Then, have your teacher or one of your peers look over the paper for you to correct any errors and bring clarity to any of the unclear sections. Once this is complete, make the necessary changes to your paper to create your final draft.

The In-depth Project

For the in-depth project, the student will follow the same steps as they did in the science fair project. However, during the high school years, they will go deeper with each step. For example, in middle school, they may have had only five references, whereas in high school, they will need around fifteen to twenty references for their research. The in-depth project should also be a semester long process, rather than several weeks.

So, let's say the student chooses to do an in-depth project involving hydroponics. They want to know if the use of hydroponics will increase plant yield. Their hypothesis, which is supported by their research, states that "Hydroponics produces a superior yield compared to traditional growing methods." For their experiment, they set up two growing environments—one in potting soil and one using hydroponics. At the middle school level, the students would have only used one type of plant observed over two to three weeks. Now, for the in-depth project, they will use multiple types of plants, such as a flower, a grass, a lettuce, and a vegetable, which they allow to grow for two to three months. The students will still need to record their observations and data daily.

Once their experiment is completed, the students will use their mathematical knowledge to analyze and report their findings. Their conclusions will be much more in depth and will include their own inferences about the findings. Once their project is complete, the student should each give a ten to fifteen minute oral presentation explaining their projects and their results.

More Information

For more information on how to do a science fair project, please read the following:

- *The Science Fair Project: A Step-by-Step Guide* by Brad and Paige Hudson
- The Science Fair Project Session: https://elementalscience.com/blogs/news/science-fair

The Research Report

The research report process should take the students about half the year to complete. Begin by having every student pick a topic and research the topic, finding out as much material as they can. They can look in biological abstracts, Google Scholar, reference books, and encyclopedias. As they find information, have them take notes that are separated into subtopics. We recommend that they put the different pieces of information on index cards that are numbered for each reference and subtopic. However, if you want the students to use a computer program rather than hand-written notes, we recommend RefWorks, which is widely used as a reference software in colleges today.

The next step is to have the students write their thesis statements. The purpose of the thesis statement is to give a focus to the paper. Their statements should give their point of view or slant on the topic. You can ask them the following questions to help them craft a thesis statement:

- What do you know currently about the topic?
- What are questions that you have about the topic?
- How do you feel about the topic?

This is a fluid process, so their thesis statements may need to be revised several times before the first draft is written.

After the students have written their thesis statements, they each needs to create an outline for their papers from the information that they gathered. Their papers needs to have three sections:

1. Introduction – This section gives a brief look at the topic, states their thesis statement, and explains why they choose the topic.
2. Body – This is the main part of their paper and contains multiple paragraphs full of information that supports the thesis statement. The body should include several quotes from experts or excerpts from their research that give credence to the thesis statement about the topic.
3. Conclusion – This section will restate the thesis statement, summarize the supporting information, and apply it to today.

After you have approved their outline, have each student turn in a rough draft of the paper. If they are not familiar with writing research papers, you may want to have them turn in multiple drafts. Either way, the final research report should be six to eight pages in length (double-spaced). You are looking to make sure that the paper is written in the third person, that it uses the correct MLA style documentation, and that the paper has a strong thesis statement with good supporting evidence.

Chemistry for High School

Unit 1 - Introduction to Chemistry

Week 1 Notes - Introduction to Chemistry

Textbook Assignments

Reading

🕮 *CK-12 Chemistry* Sections 1.1, 1.2

Written

After you finish reading, answer questions #1-4 in section 1.1 and #1-6 in section 1.2 and file your work in the reading section of your science notebook. Then, define the following terms in the glossary section of your science notebook:

- ☐ Analytical Chemistry
- ☐ Biochemistry
- ☐ Macroscopic
- ☐ Pure Chemistry
- ☐ Control Group
- ☐ Dependent Variable
- ☐ Independent Variable
- ☐ Hypothesis

Experiment - Setup A Lab Notebook

Purpose

The purpose of this lab is to familiarize you with how to setup a lab notebook and prepare your lab notebook for use in the course.

Pre-Reading

Read the background and procedure sections for the "Setup A Lab Notebook" on pg. 12 in *The Home Scientist Chemistry Laboratory Manual.*

Procedure

✓ Do the lab entitled "Setup A Lab Notebook" on pg. 12 in *The Home Scientist Chemistry Laboratory Manual.*

Lab Notebook

☞ Write down on a sheet of paper or type out your notes as you do the experiment. After you are done, print out your lab notes and add them to the lab section of your science notebook.

Lab Questions

There are no lab questions for this week.

Online Lab

☞ There is no online lab scheduled for this week.

Events in Science

Current Events

Find a current events article relating to the field of chemistry and complete the article summary sheet found on pg. 245 of the Appendix. Once you are done, add the sheet to the events section of your science notebook.

Historical Figures

- 🕒 Begin to research the life and work of Dimitri Mendeleev, who orignally laid out the first version of the periodic table. You will have five weeks to complete your research. After that, you will have three weeks to prepare a two to three page paper on this scientist and his contributions to the field of chemsitry.

Hands-on Activity

Optional Hands-on

- ✂ Use a bit of chemistry to mix up a batch of homemade ice cream! You will need ½ cup of heavy cream, ½ cup of milk, 1 tablespoon of sugar, ½ teaspoon of vanilla, 1 quart size ziploc plastic bag, 2 cups of crushed ice, 1 gallon size ziploc plastic bag, and ½ cup of rock salt. Add the cream, milk, sugar, and vanilla to the quart size baggie. Close the baggie and shake it vigorously to mix well. Next, add the ice and rock salt to the gallon size baggie, mix well, and then nestle the quart size bag into the ice mixture. Seal the large baggie up tightly and begin massaging and shaking the baggies! (*Note—It will take about 10 to 15 minutes for ice cream to form. You can use a towel or oven mitt to hold the large baggie as you shake it, if it gets too cold to handle.*)

Week 1 Supply List

Weekly Experiment	
Supplies from CK01B Chemistry Kit	❒ None
Additional Supplies From Home	❒ None
Hands-on Activity	
Supplies Needed	❒ Heavy cream, Milk, Sugar, Vanilla, 1 Quart size ziploc plastic bag, Crushed ice, 1 Gallon size ziploc plastic bag, Rock salt

Week 1	Unit 1 (Honors Course)				5-Day
Weekly Topic					
➔ This week will look at the principles of chemistry.					
	Day 1	Day 2	Day 3	Day 4	Day 5
Textbook and Experiment	❒ Read *CK-12 Chemistry* Section 1.1.	❒ Read *CK-12 Chemistry* Section 1.2.	❒ Read the background and procedure sections for the week's lab.	❒ Do the "Setup A Lab Notebook" lab on pg. 12 in *The Home Scientist Chemistry Laboratory Manual.*	❒ Do the optional Hands-on Assignment - Homemade Ice Cream.
Writing	❒ Add the vocabulary to the glossary section of your science notebook.	❒ Answer the assigned questions in the reading section of your science notebook.		❒ Record what you have done in the lab section of your science notebook.	❒ Complete the lab review questions for the week.
Events in Science	❒ Choose one of the Events in Science assignments to do and add your work to the events section of your science notebook.				
Other Notes					

Week 1	Unit 1 (Standard Course)			4-Day
Weekly Topic				
➔ This week will look at the principles of chemistry.				
	Day 1	Day 2	Day 3	Day 4
Textbook and Experiment	❐ Read *CK-12 Chemistry* Section 1.1.	❐ Read *CK-12 Chemistry* Section 1.2.	❐ Read the background and procedure sections for the week's lab.	❐ Do the "Setup A Lab Notebook" lab on pg. 12 in *The Home Scientist Chemistry Laboratory Manual.*
Writing	❐ Add the vocabulary to the glossary section of your science notebook.	❐ Answer the assigned questions in the reading section of your science notebook.		❐ Record what you have done in the lab section of your science notebook.

Other Notes

Week 1	Unit 1 (Survey Course)	2-Day
Weekly Topic		
➔ This week will look at the principles of chemistry.		
	Day 1	Day 2
Textbook	❒ Read *CK-12 Chemistry* Section 1.1.	❒ Read *CK-12 Chemistry* Section 1.2.
Writing	❒ Add the vocabulary to the glossary section of your science notebook.	❒ Answer the assigned questions in the reading section of your science notebook.
Events in Science	❒ Choose one of the Events in Science assignments to do and add your work to the events section of your science notebook.	
Other Notes		

Week 2 Notes - Matter and Change

Textbook Assignments

Reading

📖 *CK-12 Chemistry* Sections 2.1, 2.2, 2.3

Written

After you finish reading, answer questions #1,3,5 in section 2.1, questions #1-4 in section 2.2, and questions #4-7 in section 2.3. File your work in the reading section of your science notebook. Then, define the following terms in the glossary section of your science notebook:

- ☐ Intensive Property
- ☐ Extensive Property
- ☐ Volume
- ☐ Distillation
- ☐ Heterogeneous Mixture
- ☐ Homogeneous Mixture
- ☐ Precipitate
- ☐ Product
- ☐ Reactant
- ☐ Phase

Experiment - Solubility As A Function of Temperature

Purpose

The purpose of this lab is to examine the solubility as a function of temperature

Pre-Reading

- Read the background and procedure sections for the "Solubility as a Function of Temperature" lab on pg. 35 in *The Home Scientist Chemistry Laboratory Manual.*

Procedure

- ✓ Do the lab entitled "Solubility as a Function of Temperature" on pg. 35 in *The Home Scientist Chemistry Laboratory Manual.*

Lab Notebook

- ☞ Write down on a sheet of paper or type out your notes as you do the experiment. After you are done, print out your lab notes and add them to the lab section of your science notebook.

Lab Questions

- Complete the review questions of the "Solubility as a Function of Temperature" lab on pg. 41 in *The Home Scientist Chemistry Laboratory Manual.* Record the answers in the lab section of your science notebook.

Online Lab - Lab 3: Counting by Measuring Mass

Purpose

The purpose of this online lab is to determine the mass of several samples of chemical elements and compounds and to use the data to count atoms.

Pre-Reading

- Print and read the section of the workbook for the "Counting by Measuring Mass" online lab.

Procedure

- ✓ Do the lab entitled "Counting by Measuring Mass" and answer the questions as you work through the online lab.

Lab Notebook

- ☞ Add the completed workbook pages that were printed to the lab notebook.

Events in Science

Current Events

- 🕒 Find a current events article relating to the field of chemistry and complete the article summary sheet found on pg. 245 of the Appendix. Once you are done, add the sheet to the events section of your science notebook.

Historical Figures

- 🕒 Continue to research the life and work of Dmitri Mendeleev.

Hands-on Activity

Optional Hands-on

- ✂ Watch water change from a solid to a liquid to a gas. You will need a cup, ice cubes, a pot, and a thermometer. Fill a small pot halfway with ice cubes. Place the pot on a burner and turn the burner on medium heat. Observe the thermometer as the ice begins to melt and record the temperature once all the ice melts. Continue to heat the water, observing the temperature on the thermometer as it heats up. Once you begin to see the water boiling and observe the presence of steam, record your last temperature measurement. Turn the burner off and remove the pot from the burner.

Week 2 Supply List

Weekly Experiment	
Supplies from CK01B Chemistry Kit	❒ Goggles, Beaker-250 mL, Thermometer
Additional Supplies From Home	❒ Gloves, Balance (optional), Microwave oven, Oven - baking dish, Refrigerator/freezer, Measuring spoons (optional), Soda bottle- pint/500 mL (empty and clean), Storage container (wide mouth, with lid), Sodium bicarbonate (baking soda), Distilled water
Hands-on Activity	
Supplies Needed	❒ Cup, Ice cubes, Pot, Thermometer

Week 2	Unit 1 (Honors Course)				5-Day
Weekly Topic					
➔ This week will look at matter and changes to matter.					
	Day 1	Day 2	Day 3	Day 4	Day 5
Textbook and Experiment	❒ Read *CK-12 Chemistry* Sections 2.1 and 2.2.	❒ Read *CK-12 Chemistry* Section 2.3.	❒ Read the background and procedure sections for the week's lab.	❒ Do the "Solubility as a Function of Temperature" lab on pg. 35 in *The Home Scientist Chemistry Laboratory Manual.*	❒ Do the optional Hands-on Assignment - Changes in State.
Writing	❒ Add the vocabulary to the glossary section of your science notebook.	❒ Answer the assigned questions in the reading section of your science notebook.	❒ Take the Chapter 1 Test from *CK-12 Chemistry.*	❒ Record what you have done in the lab section of your science notebook.	❒ Complete the lab review questions for the week.
Events in Science	❒ Choose one of the Events in Science assignments to do and add your work to the events section of your science notebook.				
Other Notes					

Week 2	Unit 1 (Standard Course)			4-Day
Weekly Topic				
➔ This week will look at matter and changes to matter.				
	Day 1	Day 2	Day 3	Day 4
Textbook and Experiment	❒ Read *CK-12 Chemistry* Sections 2.1 and 2.2.	❒ Read *CK-12 Chemistry* Section 2.3.	❒ Read the background and procedure sections for the week's lab.	❒ Do the "Solubility as a Function of Temperature" lab on pg. 35 in *The Home Scientist Chemistry Laboratory Manual.* **OR** ❒ Do the online lab "Counting by Measuring Mass."
Writing	❒ Add the vocabulary to the glossary section of your science notebook.	❒ Answer the assigned questions in the reading section of your science notebook.	❒ Take the Chapter 1 Test from *CK-12 Chemistry.*	❒ Record what you have done in the lab section of your science notebook.

Other Notes

Week 2	Unit 1 (Survey Course)	2-Day
Weekly Topic		
➔ This week will look at matter and changes to matter.		
	Day 1	**Day 2**
Textbook	❒ Read *CK-12 Chemistry* Sections 2.1 and 2.2.	❒ Read *CK-12 Chemistry* Section 2.3.
Writing	❒ Add the vocabulary to the glossary section of your science notebook. ❒ Take the Chapter 1 Test from *CK-12 Chemistry.*	❒ Answer the assigned questions in the reading section of your science notebook.
Events in Science	❒ Choose one of the Events in Science assignments to do and add your work to the events section of your science notebook.	
Other Notes		

Week 3 Notes - Measurements

Textbook Assignments

Reading

📖 *CK-12 Chemistry* Section 3.1, 3.2, 3.3

Written

After you finish reading, answer questions #1-4 in section 3.1, #1-6 in section 3.2, and #1-5 in section 3.3. File your work in the reading section of your science notebook. Then, define the following terms in the glossary section of your science notebook:

- ☐ International System of Units (SI)
- ☐ Joule
- ☐ Kinetic Energy
- ☐ Scientific Notation
- ☐ Conversion Factor
- ☐ Dimensional Analysis
- ☐ Accepted Value
- ☐ Derived Unit
- ☐ pH
- ☐ Polarity
- ☐ Accuracy
- ☐ Precision

Experiment - Conductance of Ionic and Molecular Solutes

Purpose

The purpose of this lab is to examine the conductance of ionic and molecular solutes.

Pre-Reading

Read the background and procedure sections for the "Conductance of Ionic and Molecular Solutes" lab on pg. 42 in *The Home Scientist Chemistry Laboratory Manual.*

Procedure

✓ Do the lab entitled "Conductance of Ionic and Molecular Solutes" on pg. 42 in *The Home Scientist Chemistry Laboratory Manual.*

Lab Notebook

☞ Write down on a sheet of paper or type out your notes as you do the experiment. After you are done, print out your lab notes and add them to the lab section of your science notebook.

Lab Questions

Complete the review questions of the "Conductance of Ionic and Molecular Solutes" lab on pg. 48 in *The Home Scientist Chemistry Laboratory Manual.* Record the answers in the lab section of your science notebook.

Online Lab - Lab 2: Names and Formulas of Ionic Compounds

Purpose

The purpose of this online lab is to observe the formation of compounds and write their names and formulas.

Pre-Reading

- Print and read the section of the workbook for the "Names and Formulas of Ionic Compounds" online lab.

Procedure

- ✓ Do the lab entitled "Names and Formulas of Ionic Compounds" and answer the questions as you work through the online lab.

Lab Notebook

- Add the completed workbook pages that were printed to the lab notebook.

Events in Science

Current Events

- Find a current events article relating to the field of chemistry and complete the article summary sheet found on pg. 245 of the Appendix. Once you are done, add the sheet to the events section of your science notebook.

Historical Figures

- Continue to research the life and work of Dmitri Mendeleev.

Hands-on Activity

Optional Hands-on

- Practice units of measurements using the information in the following post: https://elementalscience.com/blogs/science-activities/units-of-measurement.

Week 3 Supply List

Weekly Experiment	
Supplies from CK01B Chemistry Kit	❒ Goggles, Beaker-250 mL, Beaker-100 mL, Centrifuge tube-50 mL, Pipettes, Reaction plate 24-well, Spatula, Acetic acid 6M, Ammonia 6M, Hydrochloric acid 6M, Magnesium sulfate, Sodium hydroxide 6M
Additional Supplies From Home	❒ Gloves, Digital multimeter (DMM) with probes, Microwave oven, Paper towels, Soda bottle (clean and dry), Sucrose (table sugar), Distilled water
Hands-on Activity	
Supplies Needed	❒ None

Week 3	Unit 1 (Honors Course)				5-Day
Weekly Topic					
➔ This week will look at units of measurement.					
	Day 1	Day 2	Day 3	Day 4	Day 5
Textbook and Experiment	❐ Read *CK-12 Chemistry* Sections 3.1 and 3.2.	❐ Read *CK-12 Chemistry* Section 3.3.	❐ Read the background and procedure sections for the week's lab.	❐ Do the "Conductance of Ionic and Molecular Solutes" lab on pg. 42 in *The Home Scientist Chemistry Laboratory Manual*.	❐ Do the optional Hands-on Assignment - Units of Measurement.
Writing	❐ Add the vocabulary to the glossary section of your science notebook.	❐ Answer the assigned questions in the reading section of your science notebook.	❐ Take the Chapter 2 Test from *CK-12 Chemistry*.	❐ Record what you have done in the lab section of your science notebook.	❐ Complete the lab review questions for the week.
Events in Science	❐ Choose one of the Events in Science assignments to do and add your work to the events section of your science notebook.				
Other Notes					

Week 3	Unit 1 (Standard Course)			4-Day
Weekly Topic				
➔ This week will look at units of measurement.				
	Day 1	Day 2	Day 3	Day 4
Textbook and Experiment	❒ Read *CK-12 Chemistry* Sections 3.1 and 3.2.	❒ Read *CK-12 Chemistry* Section 3.3.	❒ Read the background and procedure sections for the week's lab.	❒ Do the "Conductance of Ionic and Molecular Solutes" lab on pg. 42 in *The Home Scientist Chemistry Laboratory Manual.* **OR** ❒ Do the online lab "Names and Formulas of Ionic Compounds."
Writing	❒ Add the vocabulary to the glossary section of your science notebook.	❒ Answer the assigned questions in the reading section of your science notebook.	❒ Take the Chapter 2 Test from *CK-12 Chemistry.*	❒ Record what you have done in the lab section of your science notebook.
Other Notes				

Week 3	Unit 1 (Survey Course)	2-Day
Weekly Topic		
➔ This week will look at units of measurement.		
	Day 1	Day 2
Textbook	❐ Read *CK-12 Chemistry* Sections 3.1 and 3.2.	❐ Read *CK-12 Chemistry* Section 3.3.
Writing	❐ Add the vocabulary to the glossary section of your science notebook. ❐ Take the Chapter 2 Test from *CK-12 Chemistry.*	❐ Answer the assigned questions in the reading section of your science notebook.
Events in Science	❐ Choose one of the Events in Science assignments to do and add your work to the events section of your science notebook.	
Other Notes		

Week 4 Notes - Atomic Structure, part 1

Textbook Assignments

Reading

📖 *CK-12 Chemistry* Sections 4.1, 4.2

Written

After you finish reading, answer questions #1-6 in section 4.1 and questions #1-5 in section 4.2. File your work in the reading section of your science notebook. Then, define the following terms in the glossary section of your science notebook:

- ☐ Law of conservation of mass
- ☐ Law of definite proportions
- ☐ Cathode ray
- ☐ Cathode ray tube

Experiment - Colligative Properties of Solutions: Freezing Point Depression

Purpose

The purpose of this lab is to explain colligative properties of solutions in relation to freezing point depression.

Pre-Reading

Read the background and procedure sections for the "Colligative Properties of Solutions: Freezing Point Depression" lab on pg. 49 in *The Home Scientist Chemistry Laboratory Manual.*

Procedure

✓ Do the lab entitled "Colligative Properties of Solutions: Freezing Point Depression" on pg. 49 in *The Home Scientist Chemistry Laboratory Manual.*

Lab Notebook

☞ Write down on a sheet of paper or type out your notes as you do the experiment. After you are done, print out your lab notes and add them to the lab section of your science notebook.

Lab Questions

Complete the review questions of the "Colligative Properties of Solutions: Freezing Point Depression" lab on pg. 53 in *The Home Scientist Chemistry Laboratory Manual.* Record the answers in the lab section of your science notebook.

Online Lab - Lab 4: Thompson Cathode Ray Tube Experiment

Purpose

The purpose of this online lab is to duplicate the Thomson cathode ray tube experiment and calculate from collected data the charge to mass ratio of an electron.

Pre-Reading

Print and read the section of the workbook for the "Thompson Cathode Ray Tube Experiment" online lab.

Procedure

✓ Do the lab entitled "Thompson Cathode Ray Tube Experiment" and answer the questions as you work through the online lab.

Lab Notebook

☞ Add the completed workbook pages that were printed to the lab notebook.

Events in Science

Current Events

🕒 Find a current events article relating to the field of chemistry and complete the article summary sheet found on pg. 245 of the Appendix. Once you are done, add the sheet to the events section of your science notebook.

Historical Figures

🕒 Continue to research the life and work of Dmitri Mendeleev.

Hands-on Activity

Optional Hands-on

✂ Make a density column using the directions from the following pin: https://www.pinterest.com/pin/192036371582525962/. You will need honey, Karo syrup, liquid dish soap, water, vegetable oil, rubbing alcohol, lamp oil, and a glass jar.

Week 4 Supply List

Weekly Experiment	
Supplies from CK01B Chemistry Kit	❐ Goggles, Beaker-100 mL, Beaker-250 mL, Sharpie marking pen, Stirring rod, Test tube-16x100mm, Thermometer
Additional Supplies From Home	❐ Gloves, Balance (optional), Foam cups (or similar containers), Freezer, Measuring spoons (if no balance), Sodium chloride (table salt), Sucrose (table sugar), Distilled water, Ice (crushed or chipped)
Hands-on Activity	
Supplies Needed	❐ Honey, Karo syrup, Liquid dish soap, Water, Vegetable oil, Rubbing alcohol, Lamp oil, Glass jar

Week 4	Unit 1 (Honors Course)				5-Day
Weekly Topic					
➔ This week will begin a look at atomic structure.					
	Day 1	Day 2	Day 3	Day 4	Day 5
Textbook and Experiment	❒ Read *CK-12 Chemistry* Section 4.1.	❒ Read *CK-12 Chemistry* Section 4.2.	❒ Read the background and procedure sections for the week's lab.	❒ Do the "Colligative Properties of Solutions: Freezing Point Depression" lab on pg. 49 in *The Home Scientist Chemistry Laboratory Manual*.	❒ Do the optional Hands-on Assignment - Density Column.
Writing	❒ Add the vocabulary to the glossary section of your science notebook.	❒ Answer the assigned questions in the reading section of your science notebook.	❒ Take the Chapter 3 Test from *CK-12 Chemistry*.	❒ Record what you have done in the lab section of your science notebook.	❒ Complete the lab review questions for the week.
Events in Science	❒ Choose one of the Events in Science assignments to do and add your work to the events section of your science notebook.				
Other Notes					

Week 4	Unit 1 (Standard Course)			4-Day
Weekly Topic				
➔ This week will begin a look at atomic structure.				
	Day 1	Day 2	Day 3	Day 4
Textbook and Experiment	❒ Read *CK-12 Chemistry* Section 4.1.	❒ Read *CK-12 Chemistry* Sections 4.2.	❒ Read the background and procedure sections for the week's lab.	❒ Do the "Colligative Properties of Solutions: Freezing Point Depression" lab on pg. 49 in *The Home Scientist Chemistry Laboratory Manual.* **OR** ❒ Do the online lab "Thompson Cathode Ray Tube Experiment."
Writing	❒ Add the vocabulary to the glossary section of your science notebook.	❒ Answer the assigned questions in the reading section of your science notebook.	❒ Take the Chapter 3 Test from *CK-12 Chemistry.*	❒ Record what you have done in the lab section of your science notebook.
Other Notes				

Week 4	Unit 1 (Survey Course)	2-Day
Weekly Topic		
➔ This week will begin a look at atomic structure.		
	Day 1	**Day 2**
Textbook	❒ Read *CK-12 Chemistry* Section 4.1.	❒ Read *CK-12 Chemistry* Sections 4.2.
Writing	❒ Add the vocabulary to the glossary section of your science notebook. ❒ Take the Chapter 3 Test from *CK-12 Chemistry.*	❒ Answer the assigned questions in the reading section of your science notebook.
Events in Science	❒ Choose one of the Events in Science assignments to do and add your work to the events section of your science notebook.	
Other Notes		

Week 5 Notes - Atomic Structure, part 2

Textbook Assignments

Reading

📖 *CK-12 Chemistry* Section 4.3

Written

After you finish reading, answer questions #1-12 in section 4.3 and file your work in the reading section of your science notebook. Then, define the following terms in the glossary section of your science notebook:

- ☐ Atomic Mass
- ☐ Atomic Mass Unit
- ☐ Atomic Number
- ☐ Isotope
- ☐ Mass Number
- ☐ Nuclide

Experiment - Determining the Effect of Temperature, Concentration, and Surface Area on Reaction Rates

Purpose

The purpose of this lab is to explain effects of temperature, concentration, and surface area on reaction rates.

Pre-Reading

- Read the background and procedure sections for the "Determining the Effect of Temperature, Concentration, and Surface Area on Reaction Rates" lab on pg. 94 in *The Home Scientist Chemistry Laboratory Manual.*

Procedure

- ✓ Do the lab entitled "Determining the Effect of Temperature, Concentration, and Surface Area on Reaction Rates" on pg. 94 in *The Home Scientist Chemistry Laboratory Manual.*

Lab Notebook

- ☞ Write down on a sheet of paper or type out your notes as you do the experiment. After you are done, print out your lab notes and add them to the lab section of your science notebook.

Lab Questions

- Complete the review questions of the "Determining the Effect of Temperature, Concentration, and Surface Area on Reaction Rates" lab on pg. 99 in *The Home Scientist Chemistry Laboratory Manual.* Record the answers in the lab section of your science notebook.

Online Lab - Lab 5: Millikan Oil Drop Experiment

Purpose

The purpose of this online lab is to duplicate the Millikan Oil Drop experiment and determine the charge on an electron.

Pre-Reading

- Print and read the section of the workbook for the "Millikan Oil Drop Experiment" online lab.

Procedure

- ✓ Do the lab entitled "Millikan Oil Drop Experiment" and answer the questions as you work through the online lab.

Lab Notebook

- Add the completed workbook pages that were printed to the lab notebook.

Events in Science

Current Events

- Find a current events article relating to the field of chemistry and complete the article summary sheet found on pg. 245 of the Appendix. Once you are done, add the sheet to the events section of your science notebook.

Historical Figures

- Continue to research the life and work of Dmitri Mendeleev.

Hands-on Activity

Optional Hands-on

- Play a game of *Atoms and Isotopes*. You can download this game free from here: https://elementalscience.com/blogs/science-activities/60317571-free-chemistry-game. You will also need blue, brown, and red colored beads or mini-M&M's, at least thirty of each. You can also play "Build an Atom" online here: http://www.orau.org/center-for-science-education/files/build-an-atom/.

Week 5 Supply List

Weekly Experiment	
Supplies from CK01B Chemistry Kit	❒ Goggles, Beaker-50 mL, Beaker-100 mL, Beaker-250 mL, Thermometer, Sodium bicarbonate tablets
Additional Supplies From Home	❒ Gloves, Microwave oven, Refrigerator, Soda bottles (empty), Watch or clock with second hand, Distilled white vinegar (supermarket), Graphing paper/calculator/software
Hands-on Activity	
Supplies Needed	❒ Blue, brown, and red colored beads or mini-M&M's (at least 30 of each), *Atoms and Isotopes* game board and cards

Week 5	Unit 1 (Honors Course)				5-Day
Weekly Topic					
➔ This week will wrap up a look at atomic structure.					
	Day 1	Day 2	Day 3	Day 4	Day 5
Textbook and Experiment	❒ Read *CK-12 Chemistry* Section 4.3.		❒ Read the background and procedure sections for the week's lab.	❒ Do the "Determining the Effect of Temperature, Concentration, and Surface Area on Reaction Rates" lab on pg. 94 in *The Home Scientist Chemistry Laboratory Manual.*	❒ Do the optional Hands-on Assignment - Atoms and Isotopes Game.
Writing	❒ Add the vocabulary to the glossary section of your science notebook.	❒ Answer the assigned questions in the reading section of your science notebook.	❒ Take the Chapter 4 Test from *CK-12 Chemistry.*	❒ Record what you have done in the lab section of your science notebook.	❒ Complete the lab review questions for the week.
Events in Science	❒ Choose one of the Events in Science assignments to do and add your work to the events section of your science notebook.				
Other Notes					

Week 5	Unit 1 (Standard Course)			4-Day
Weekly Topic				
➔ This week will wrap up a look at atomic structure.				
	Day 1	Day 2	Day 3	Day 4
Textbook and Experiment	❒ Read *CK-12 Chemistry* Section 4.3.		❒ Read the background and procedure sections for the week's lab.	❒ Do the "Determining the Effect of Temperature, Concentration, and Surface Area on Reaction Rates" lab on pg. 94 in *The Home Scientist Chemistry Laboratory Manual.* **OR** ❒ Do the online lab "Millikan Oil Drop Experiment."
Writing	❒ Add the vocabulary to the glossary section of your science notebook.	❒ Answer the assigned questions in the reading section of your science notebook.	❒ Take the Chapter 4 Test from *CK-12 Chemistry.*	❒ Record what you have done in the lab section of your science notebook.
Other Notes				

Week 5	Unit 1 (Survey Course)	2-Day
Weekly Topic		
➔ This week will wrap up a look at atomic structure.		
	Day 1	Day 2
Textbook	❐ Read *CK-12 Chemistry* Section 4.3.	❐ Take the Chapter 4 Test from *CK-12 Chemistry.*
Writing	❐ Add the vocabulary to the glossary section of your science notebook.	❐ Answer the assigned questions in the reading section of your science notebook.
Events in Science	❐ Choose one of the Events in Science assignments to do and add your work to the events section of your science notebook.	
Other Notes		

Week 6 Notes - Electrons, part 1

Textbook Assignments

Reading

📖 *CK-12 Chemistry* Sections 5.1, 5.2

Written

After you finish reading, answer questions #1-10 in section 5.1 and questions #1-7 in 5.2. File your work in the reading section of your science notebook. Then, define the following terms in the glossary section of your science notebook:

- [ ] Atomic Emission Spectrum
- [ ] Electromagnetic Radiation
- [ ] Photoelectric Effect
- [ ] Quantum
- [ ] Photon
- [ ] Heisenberg Uncertainty Principle
- [ ] Quantum Mechanics
- [ ] Quantum Number
- [ ] Principle Quantum Number

Experiment - Recrystallization

Purpose

The purpose of this lab is to learn how to seperate mixtures by recrystaliaztion.

Pre-Reading

Read the background and procedure sections for the "Recrystallization" lab on pg. 18 in *The Home Scientist Chemistry Laboratory Manual.*

Procedure

✓ Do the lab entitled "Recrystallization" on pg. 18 in *The Home Scientist Chemistry Laboratory Manual.*

Lab Notebook

☞ Write down on a sheet of paper or type out your notes as you do the experiment. After you are done, print out your lab notes and add them to the lab section of your science notebook.

Lab Questions

Complete the review questions of the "Recrystallization " lab on pg. 23 in *The Home Scientist Chemistry Laboratory Manual.* Record the answers in the lab section of your science notebook.

Online Lab - Lab 6: Atomic Structure and Rutherford's Experiment

Purpose

The purpose of this online lab is to discover how the physical properties, such as size and shape, of an object can be measured by indirect means and to duplicate the gold foil experiment of Ernest Rutherford.

Pre-Reading

- Print and read the section of the workbook for the "Atomic Structure and Rutherford's Experiment" online lab.

Procedure

- ✓ Do the lab entitled "Atomic Structure and Rutherford's Experiment" and answer the questions as you work through the online lab.

Lab Notebook

- Add the completed workbook pages that were printed to the lab notebook.

Events in Science

Current Events

- Find a current events article relating to the field of chemistry and complete the article summary sheet found on pg. 245 of the Appendix. Once you are done, add the sheet to the events section of your science notebook.

Historical Figures

- Begin to work on your paper on the life and work of Dimitri Mendeleev. This week, aim to complete your outline. See pg. 14 for more directions. You will have three weeks to complete this paper.

Hands-on Activity

Optional Hands-on

- Make a model atom using four pipe cleaners and nine round beads in three different colors, three of each color. Select which beads will be electrons, protons, and neutrons. Next, string three proton beads and three neutron beads on one of the pipe cleaners, alternating between the two. Once done, wrap the portion of the pipe cleaner into a ball to form a nucleus, leaving a straight end to connect to the electron rings. To make the electron rings, place one electron bead on a pipe cleaner and twist the pipe cleaner closed to form a ring. Repeat this process two more times, so that there are three electron rings. Finally, fit the rings inside each other and then hang the nucleus ball in the center, using the pipe cleaner tail from the nucleus-forming step and twist to hold the rings together.

Week 6 Supply List

Weekly Experiment	
Supplies from CK01B Chemistry Kit	❒ Goggles, Beakers-250, 100, and 50 mL, Hydrochloric acid, Stirring rod, Thermometer
Additional Supplies From Home	❒ Gloves, Microwave oven, Oven mitts or tongs, Paper (sheet of copy paper or similar), Paper towels, Refrigerator/freezer, Tablespoon (measuring or standard), Teaspoon (measuring or standard), Sodium bicarbonate (baking soda), Sodium chloride (table salt)
Hands-on Activity	
Supplies Needed	❒ 4 Pipe cleaners, 9 Round beads in three different colors (3 of each color)

Week 6	Unit 1 (Honors Course)				5-Day
Weekly Topic					
➔ This week will begin a look at electrons.					
	Day 1	Day 2	Day 3	Day 4	Day 5
Textbook and Experiment	❒ Read *CK-12 Chemistry* Section 5.1.	❒ Read *CK-12 Chemistry* Section 5.2.	❒ Read the background and procedure sections for the week's lab.	❒ Do the "Recrystallization" lab on pg. 18 in *The Home Scientist Chemistry Laboratory Manual.*	❒ Do the optional Hands-on Assignment - Atomic Model.
Writing	❒ Add the vocabulary to the glossary section of your science notebook.	❒ Answer the assigned questions in the reading section of your science notebook.		❒ Record what you have done in the lab section of your science notebook.	❒ Complete the lab review questions for the week.
Events in Science	❒ Choose one of the Events in Science assignments to do and add your work to the events section of your science notebook.				
Other Notes					

Week 6	Unit 1 (Standard Course)			4-Day
Weekly Topic				
➔ This week will begin a look at electrons.				
	Day 1	Day 2	Day 3	Day 4
Textbook and Experiment	❒ Read *CK-12 Chemistry* Section 5.1.	❒ Read *CK-12 Chemistry* Section 5.2.	❒ Read the background and procedure sections for the week's lab.	❒ Do the "Recrystallization" lab on pg. 18 in *The Home Scientist Chemistry Laboratory Manual.* **OR** ❒ Do the online lab "Atomic Structure and Rutherford's Experiment."
Writing	❒ Add the vocabulary to the glossary section of your science notebook.	❒ Answer the assigned questions in the reading section of your science notebook.		❒ Record what you have done in the lab section of your science notebook.

Other Notes

Week 6	Unit 1 (Survey Course)	2-Day
Weekly Topic		
➔ This week will begin a look at electrons.		
	Day 1	Day 2
Textbook	❒ Read *CK-12 Chemistry* Section 5.1.	❒ Read *CK-12 Chemistry* Section 5.2.
Writing	❒ Add the vocabulary to the glossary section of your science notebook.	❒ Answer the assigned questions in the reading section of your science notebook.
Events in Science	❒ Choose one of the Events in Science assignments to do and add your work to the events section of your science notebook.	
Other Notes		

Week 7 Notes - Electrons, part 2

Textbook Assignments

Reading

📖 *CK-12 Chemistry* Sections 5.3

Written

After you finish reading, answer questions #1-12 in section 5.3. File your work in the reading section of your science notebook. Then, define the following terms in the glossary section of your science notebook:

- ☐ Aufbau Principle
- ☐ Electron Configuration
- ☐ Hund's Rule
- ☐ Noble Gas Notation
- ☐ Pauli Exclusion Principle
- ☐ Valence Electron

Experiment - Chromatography

Purpose

The purpose of this lab is to explain and experiment with the process of chromatography.

Pre-Reading

Read the background and procedure sections for the "Chromatography" lab on pg. 24 in *The Home Scientist Chemistry Laboratory Manual.*

Procedure

✓ Do the lab entitled "Chromatography" on pg. 24 in *The Home Scientist Chemistry Laboratory Manual.*

Lab Notebook

Write down on a sheet of paper or type out your notes as you do the experiment. After you are done, print out your lab notes and add them to the lab section of your science notebook.

Lab Questions

Complete the review questions of the "Chromatography" lab on pg. 30 in *The Home Scientist Chemistry Laboratory Manual.* Record the answers in the lab section of your science notebook.

Online Lab - Lab 10: Electronic State Energy Levels

Purpose

The purpose of this online lab is to understand the origins of Quantum Theory using a spectrometer to observe the emission spectrum of several gases.

Pre-Reading

Print and read the section of the workbook for the "Electronic State Energy Levels" online lab.

Procedure

- ✓ Do the lab entitled "Electronic State Energy Levels" and answer the questions as you work through the online lab.

Lab Notebook

- ☞ Add the completed workbook pages that were printed to the lab notebook.

Events in Science

Current Events

- 🕒 Find a current events article relating to the field of chemistry and complete the article summary sheet found on pg. 245 of the Appendix. Once you are done, add the sheet to the events section of your science notebook.

Historical Figures

- 🕒 Continue work on your paper on the life and work of Dimitri Mendeleev. This week, aim to complete your rough draft. See pg. 14 for more directions.

Hands-on Activity

Optional Hands-on

- ✂ Make a model of the p-orbital using six small balloons and tape. Begin by blowing up the six balloons. Then, tape two of the balloons together at the place you tied them off and repeat this process with the remaining four balloons so that you have 3 sets of attached balloons. Finally, tape the three sets together at their connection points to form the shape of the p-orbital.

Week 7 Supply List

Weekly Experiment	
Supplies from CK01B Chemistry Kit	❒ Goggles, Centrifuge tube-50 mL, Chromatography paper, Pipettes, Ruler, Sharpie marking pen, Copper(II) sulfate, Lead(II) acetate, Potassium iodide
Additional Supplies From Home	❒ Gloves, Cotton swabs, Pencil, Hair dryer (optional), Paper towels, Scissors, Toothpicks-plastic, Transparent tape, Additional felt-tip pens (optional), Isopropyl alcohol (70%, 91%, or 99%)
Hands-on Activity	
Supplies Needed	❒ 6 Small balloons, Tape

Week 7	Unit 1 (Honors Course)				5-Day
Weekly Topic					
➔ This week will wrap up a look at electrons.					
	Day 1	Day 2	Day 3	Day 4	Day 5
Textbook and Experiment	❒ Read *CK-12 Chemistry* Section 5.3.		❒ Read the background and procedure sections for the week's lab.	❒ Do the "Chromatography" lab on pg. 24 in *The Home Scientist Chemistry Laboratory Manual*.	❒ Do the optional Hands-on Assignment - P-Orbital Model.
Writing	❒ Add the vocabulary to the glossary section of your science notebook.	❒ Answer the assigned questions in the reading section of your science notebook.	❒ Take the Chapter 5 Test from *CK-12 Chemistry*.	❒ Record what you have done in the lab section of your science notebook.	❒ Complete the lab review questions for the week.
Events in Science	❒ Choose one of the Events in Science assignments to do and add your work to the events section of your science notebook.				
Other Notes					

Week 7	Unit 1 (Standard Course)			4-Day
Weekly Topic				
➔ This week will wrap up a look at electrons.				
	Day 1	Day 2	Day 3	Day 4
Textbook and Experiment	❒ Read *CK-12 Chemistry* Section 5.3.		❒ Read the background and procedure sections for the week's lab.	❒ Do the "Chromatography" lab on pg. 24 in *The Home Scientist Chemistry Laboratory Manual.* **OR** ❒ Do the online lab "Electronic State Energy Levels."
Writing	❒ Add the vocabulary to the glossary section of your science notebook.	❒ Answer the assigned questions in the reading section of your science notebook.	❒ Take the Chapter 5 Test from *CK-12 Chemistry.*	❒ Record what you have done in the lab section of your science notebook.
Other Notes				

Week 7	Unit 1 (Survey Course)	2-Day
Weekly Topic		
➔ This week will wrap up a look at electrons.		
	Day 1	**Day 2**
Textbook	❒ Read *CK-12 Chemistry* Section 5.3.	❒ Take the Chapter 5 Test from *CK-12 Chemistry*.
Writing	❒ Add the vocabulary to the glossary section of your science notebook.	❒ Answer the assigned questions in the reading section of your science notebook.
Events in Science	❒ Choose one of the Events in Science assignments to do and add your work to the events section of your science notebook.	
Other Notes		

Week 8 Notes - The Periodic Table

Textbook Assignments

Reading

📖 *CK-12 Chemistry* Section 6.1, 6.2, 6.3

Written

After you finish reading, answer questions #1-5 in section 6.1, questions #1-9 in section 6.2, and questions #6-8 in section 6.3 and file your work in the reading section of your science notebook. Then, define the following terms in the glossary section of your science notebook:

- ☐ Period
- ☐ Periodic Law
- ☐ Intertransition Metal
- ☐ Representative Elements
- ☐ Electron Affinity
- ☐ Electronegativity
- ☐ Ionization Energy

Experiment - Full Lab Report

Lab Notebook

☞ This week, choose one of your previous labs and write a full lab report. See pg. 10 for directions on how to write a full lab report. Add your completed write-up to your lab notebook.

Online Lab - Lab 9: Diffraction Experiments

Purpose

The purpose of this online lab is to investigate the wave-particle duality of nature.

Pre-Reading

Print and read the section of the workbook for the "Diffraction Experiments" online lab.

Procedure

✓ Do the lab entitled "Diffraction Experiments" and answer the questions as you work through the online lab.

Lab Notebook

☞ Add the completed workbook pages that were printed to the lab notebook.

Events in Science

Current Events

🕒 There is no assignment for this week.

Historical Figures

🕒 There is no assignment for this week.

Hands-on Activity

Optional Hands-on

- ✂ Work on memorizing the elements found in the periodic table. You can use the following song to help: https://www.youtube.com/watch?v=VgVQKCcfwnU.

Week 8 Supply List

Weekly Experiment	
Supplies from CK01B Chemistry Kit	❐ None
Additional Supplies From Home	❐ None
Hands-on Activity	
Supplies Needed	❐ None

Week 8	Unit 1 (Honors Course)				5-Day
Weekly Topic					
➔ This week will look at the periodic table					
	Day 1	Day 2	Day 3	Day 4	Day 5
Textbook and Experiment	❒ Read *CK-12 Chemistry* Sections 6.1 and 6.2.	❒ Read *CK-12 Chemistry* Section 6.3.	❒ Work on the full lab report.	❒ Work on the full lab report.	❒ Do the optional Hands-on Assignment - Memorizing the Periodic Table.
Writing	❒ Add the vocabulary to the glossary section of your science notebook.	❒ Answer the assigned questions in the reading section of your science notebook.		❒ Take the Chapter 6 Test from *CK-12 Chemistry.*	
Other Notes					

Week 8	Unit 1 (Standard Course)			4-Day
Weekly Topic				
➔ This week will look at the periodic table.				
	Day 1	Day 2	Day 3	Day 4
Textbook and Experiment	❒ Read *CK-12 Chemistry* Sections 6.1 and 6.2.	❒ Read *CK-12 Chemistry* Section 6.3.	❒ Work on the full lab report.	❒ Work on the full lab report. **OR** ❒ Do the online lab "Electronic State Energy Levels."
Writing	❒ Add the vocabulary to the glossary section of your science notebook.	❒ Answer the assigned questions in the reading section of your science notebook.		❒ Take the Chapter 6 Test from *CK-12 Chemistry.*
Other Notes				

Week 8	Unit 1 (Survey Course)	2-Day
Weekly Topic		
➔ This week will look at the periodic table.		
	Day 1	Day 2
Textbook	❒ Read *CK-12 Chemistry* Sections 6.1 and 6.2.	❒ Read *CK-12 Chemistry* Section 6.3.
Writing	❒ Add the vocabulary to the glossary section of your science notebook.	❒ Answer the assigned questions in the reading section of your science notebook.
Other Notes		

Week 9 Notes - Nomenclature

Textbook Assignments

Reading

📖 *CK-12 Chemistry* Section 7.1, 7.2, 7.3

Written

After you finish reading, answer questions #1-6 in section 7.1, questions #1-5 in section 7.2, and questions #4-6 in section 7.3 and file your work in the reading section of your science notebook. Then, define the following terms in the glossary section of your science notebook:

- ☐ Binary Ionic Compound
- ☐ Ternary Ionic Compound
- ☐ Monatomic Ion
- ☐ Binary Molecular Compound
- ☐ Binary Acid
- ☐ Oxoacid

Experiment - Full Lab Report

Lab Notebook

☞ This week, complete the full lab report. See pg. 10 for directions on how to write a full lab report. Add your completed write-up to your lab notebook.

Online Lab - Full Lab Report

Lab Notebook

☞ This week, complete the full lab report. See pg. 10 for directions on how to write a full lab report. Add your completed write-up to your lab notebook.

Events in Science

Current Events

🕒 There is no assignment for this week.

Historical Figures

🕒 There is no assignment for this week.

Hands-on Activity

Optional Hands-on

✂ Observe the freezing points of several different liquids. To do this, you will need sample liquids (oil, fruit juice, water, saltwater, and so on), ice cube tray, instant thermometer, and access to a freezer. Fill the wells of the ice cube tray with your sample liquids and place the tray in the freezer. Check it every 10 minutes and record the temperature at which the different sample liquids freeze.

Week 9 Supply List

Weekly Experiment	
Supplies from CK01B Chemistry Kit	❒ None
Additional Supplies From Home	❒ None
Hands-on Activity	
Supplies Needed	❒ Sample liquids (oil, fruit juice, water, saltwater, and so on), Ice cube tray, Instant thermometer

Week 9	Unit 1 (Honors Course)				5-Day
Weekly Topic					
➔ This week will look at nomenclature.					
	Day 1	Day 2	Day 3	Day 4	Day 5
Textbook and Experiment	❒ Read *CK-12 Chemistry* Sections 7.1 and 7.2.	❒ Read *CK-12 Chemistry* Section 7.3.	❒ Work on the full lab report.	❒ Work on the full lab report.	❒ Do the optional Hands-on Assignment - Freezing Points
Writing	❒ Add the vocabulary to the glossary section of your science notebook.	❒ Answer the assigned questions in the reading section of your science notebook.		❒ Take the Chapter 7 Test from *CK-12 Chemistry*.	❒ Complete the lab review questions for the week.
Events in Science	❒ Choose one of the Events in Science assignments to do and add your work to the events section of your science notebook.				
Other Notes					

Week 9	Unit 1 (Standard Course)			4-Day
Weekly Topic				
➔ This week will look at nomenclature.				
	Day 1	Day 2	Day 3	Day 4
Textbook and Experiment	❒ Read *CK-12 Chemistry* Sections 7.1 and 7.2.	❒ Read *CK-12 Chemistry* Section 7.3.	❒ Work on the full lab report.	❒ Work on the full lab report.
Writing	❒ Add the vocabulary to the glossary section of your science notebook.	❒ Answer the assigned questions in the reading section of your science notebook.		❒ Take the Chapter 7 Test from *CK-12 Chemistry.*
Other Notes				

Week 9	Unit 1 (Survey Course)	2-Day
Weekly Topic		
➔ This week will look at nomenclature.		
	Day 1	Day 2
Textbook	❐ Read *CK-12 Chemistry* Sections 7.1 and 7.2.	❐ Read *CK-12 Chemistry* Section 7.3.
Writing	❐ Add the vocabulary to the glossary section of your science notebook. ❐ Take the Chapter 6 Test from *CK-12 Chemistry.*	❐ Answer the assigned questions in the reading section of your science notebook.
Events in Science	❐ Choose one of the Events in Science assignments to do and add your work to the events section of your science notebook.	
Other Notes		

Chemistry for High School

Unit 2 - Bonding and Reactions

Week 1 Notes - Ionic and Metallic Bonding

Textbook Assignments

Reading

📖 *CK-12 Chemistry* Section 8.1, 8.2, 8.3

Written

After you finish reading, answer questions #3-6 in section 8.1, questions #5-7 in section 8.2, and questions #3,5,7 in section 8.3 and file your work in the reading section of your science notebook. Then, define the following terms in the glossary section of your science notebook:

- ☐ Isoelectronic
- ☐ Octet Rule
- ☐ Coordination Number
- ☐ Formula Unit
- ☐ Metallic Bond

Experiment - Observe a Composition Reaction

Purpose

The purpose of this lab is to observe a compostion reaction in chemistry.

Pre-Reading

Read the background and procedure sections for the "Observe a Composition Reaction" lab on pg. 58 in *The Home Scientist Chemistry Laboratory Manual.*

Procedure

✓ Do the lab entitled "Observe a Compostion Reaction" on pg. 58 in *The Home Scientist Chemistry Laboratory Manual.*

Lab Notebook

☞ Write down on a sheet of paper or type out your notes as you do the experiment. After you are done, print out your lab notes and add them to the lab section of your science notebook.

Lab Questions

Complete the multiple choice section of the "Observe a Composition Reaction" lab on pg. 59 in *The Home Scientist Chemistry Laboratory Manual.* Record the answers in the lab section of your science notebook.

Online Lab - Lab 1: Flame Test for Metals

Purpose

The purpose of this online lab is to observe and identify metallic ions using flame tests.

Pre-Reading

Print and read the section of the workbook for the "Flame Test for Metals" online lab.

Procedure

✓ Do the lab entitled "Flame Test for Metals" and answer the questions as you work through the online lab.

Lab Notebook

☞ Add the completed workbook pages that were printed to the lab notebook.

Events in Science

Current Events

◷ Find a current events article relating to the field of molecular chemistry and complete the article summary sheet found on pg. 245 of the Appendix. Once you are done, add the sheet to the events section of your science notebook.

Historical Figures

◷ Begin to research the life and work of Neils Bohr, who came up with a model for the atom. You will have five weeks to complete your research. After that, you will have three weeks to prepare a two to three page paper on this scientist and his contributions to the field of chemistry.

Hands-on Activity

Optional Hands-on

✂ Make an ionic bond using cake frosting and red and yellow bite-sized candies, such as M&M's. For ionic bonding, count out nine red candies and one yellow candy. Arrange the nine red candies in a circle, so that there are two in the center with seven surrounding them. (*Be sure to leave a space for one more in the outer circle.*) These are the electrons in the outer shell of a chlorine atom. Take the one yellow candy, which represents the electron in the outer shell of a sodium atom and move it into the space in the outer circle of the chlorine electrons. Now you have an ionic bond between your sodium and chlorine atom.

Week 1 Supply List

Weekly Experiment	
Supplies from CK01B Chemistry Kit	❒ Goggles, Test tube clamp, Iron wool
Additional Supplies From Home	❒ Gloves, Butane lighter (or other flame source), Sheet of white paper
Hands-on Activity	
Supplies Needed	❒ Cake frosting, Red and yellow bite-sized candies

Week 1	Unit 2 (Honors Course)				5-Day
Weekly Topic					
➔ This week will look at ionic and metallic bonding.					
	Day 1	Day 2	Day 3	Day 4	Day 5
Textbook and Experiment	❒ Read *CK-12 Chemistry* Sections 8.1 and 8.2.	❒ Read *CK-12 Chemistry* Section 8.3.	❒ Read the background and procedure sections for the week's lab.	❒ Do the "Observe a Composition Reaction" lab on pg. 58 in *The Home Scientist Chemistry Laboratory Manual.*	❒ Do the optional Hands-on Assignment - Candy Bonding.
Writing	❒ Add the vocabulary to the glossary section of your science notebook.	❒ Answer the assigned questions in the reading section of your science notebook.		❒ Record what you have done in the lab section of your science notebook.	❒ Complete the lab review questions for the week.
Events in Science	❒ Choose one of the Events in Science assignments to do and add your work to the events section of your science notebook.				
Other Notes					

Week 1	Unit 2 (Standard Course)			4-Day
Weekly Topic				
➔ This week will look at ionic and metallic bonding.				
	Day 1	Day 2	Day 3	Day 4
Textbook and Experiment	❒ Read *CK-12 Chemistry* Sections 8.1 and 8.2.	❒ Read *CK-12 Chemistry* Section 8.3.	❒ Read the background and procedure sections for the week's lab.	❒ Do the "Observe a Composition Reaction" lab on pg. 58 in *The Home Scientist Chemistry Laboratory Manual.* **OR** ❒ Do the online lab "Flame Test for Metals."
Writing	❒ Add the vocabulary to the glossary section of your science notebook.	❒ Answer the assigned questions in the reading section of your science notebook.		❒ Record what you have done in the lab section of your science notebook.
Other Notes				

Week 1	Unit 2 (Survey Course)	2-Day
	Weekly Topic	
➔ This week will look at ionic and metallic bonding.		
	Day 1	**Day 2**
Textbook	❒ Read *CK-12 Chemistry* Sections 8.1 and 8.2.	❒ Read *CK-12 Chemistry* Section 8.3.
Writing	❒ Add the vocabulary to the glossary section of your science notebook. ❒ Take the Chapter 7 Test from *CK-12 Chemistry.*	❒ Answer the assigned questions in the reading section of your science notebook.
Events in Science	❒ Choose one of the Events in Science assignments to do and add your work to the events section of your science notebook.	
	Other Notes	

Week 2 Notes - Covalent Bonding

Textbook Assignments

Reading

📖 *CK-12 Chemistry* Section 9.1, 9.2, 9.3, 9.4

Written

After you finish reading, answer questions #6,7 in section 9.1, questions #7,8 in section 9.2, questions #1-4 in section 9.3, and questions #1-6 in 9.4 and file your work in the reading section of your science notebook. Then, define the following terms in the glossary section of your science notebook:

- ☐ Lewis Electron Dot Structure
- ☐ Diatomic Molecule
- ☐ Resonance
- ☐ Lone Pair
- ☐ Electron Domain Geometry
- ☐ VSEPR
- ☐ London Dispersion Forces
- ☐ Van der Waals Forces
- ☐ Dipole Forces
- ☐ Hybridization
- ☐ Pi-bond
- ☐ Sigma-bond

Experiment Observe a Decomposition Reaction

Purpose

The purpose of this lab is to observe a decompostion reaction.

Pre-Reading

Read the background and procedure sections for the "Observe a Decompostion Reaction" lab on pg. 60 in *The Home Scientist Chemistry Laboratory Manual.*

Procedure

✓ Do the lab entitled "Observe a Decomposition Reaction" on pg. 60 in *The Home Scientist Chemistry Laboratory Manual.*

Lab Notebook

☞ Write down on a sheet of paper or type out your notes as you do the experiment. After you are done, print out your lab notes and add them to the lab section of your science notebook.

Lab Questions

Complete the multiple choice section of the "Observe a Decomposition Reaction" lab on pg. 62 in *The Home Scientist Chemistry Laboratory Manual.* Record the answers in the lab section of your science notebook.

Online Lab - Lab 7: Atomic Emission Spectra

Purpose

The purpose of this online lab is to view atomic emission spectra and use a spectrometer to measure the wavelength.

Pre-Reading

✍ Print and read the section of the workbook for the "Atomic Emission Spectra" online lab.

Procedure

✓ Do the lab entitled "Atomic Emission Spectra" and answer the questions as you work through the online lab.

Lab Notebook

☞ Add the completed workbook pages that were printed to the lab notebook.

Events in Science

Current Events

🕒 Find a current events article relating to the field of molecular chemistry and complete the article summary sheet found on pg. 245 of the Appendix. Once you are done, add the sheet to the events section of your science notebook.

Historical Figures

🕒 Continue to research the life and work of Neils Bohr.

Hands-on Activity

Optional Hands-on

✂ Make a covalent bond using cake frosting and red and yellow bite-sized candies, such as M&M's. For covalent bonding, count out eight red candies and two yellow candies. Use the eight red candies to make a model showing the electrons in the outer shell of an oxygen atom by making a circle with six candies on the outside and two on the inside. (*Be sure to leave space for two more candies in the outer layer.*) Now take two of the yellow candies, which represent the electrons in the outer shells of the two different hydrogen atoms, and bite or cut them in half. Do the same with the two of the red candies from the outer circle you created. Then, use the frosting to glue together one half of each color to form four whole candies. Place the dual-colored candies in the outer circle of your model to represent the covalent bond that is found between oxygen and hydrogen in water.

Week 2 Supply List

Weekly Experiment	
Supplies from CK01B Chemistry Kit	❒ Goggles, Stirring rod, Test tube clamp, Test tube-16x100mm, Barium nitrate solution, Cobalt chloride test paper, Wood splint
Additional Supplies From Home	❒ Gloves, Butane lighter (or other flame source), Sodium bicarbonate (baking soda)
Hands-on Activity	
Supplies Needed	❒ Cake frosting, Red and yellow bite-sized candies

Week 2	Unit 2 (Honors Course)				5-Day
Weekly Topic					
➔ This week will look at covalent bonding.					
	Day 1	Day 2	Day 3	Day 4	Day 5
Textbook and Experiment	❐ Read *CK-12 Chemistry* Sections 9.1 and 9.2.	❐ Read *CK-12 Chemistry* Sections 9.3 and 9.4.	❐ Read the background and procedure sections for the week's lab.	❐ Do the "Observe a Decompostion Reaction" lab on pg. 60 in *The Home Scientist Chemistry Laboratory Manual.*	❐ Do the optional Hands-on Assignment - Changes in State.
Writing	❐ Add the vocabulary to the glossary section of your science notebook.	❐ Answer the assigned questions in the reading section of your science notebook.	❐ Take the Chapter 8 Test from *CK-12 Chemistry.*	❐ Record what you have done in the lab section of your science notebook.	❐ Complete the lab review questions for the week.
Events in Science	❐ Choose one of the Events in Science assignments to do and add your work to the events section of your science notebook.				
Other Notes					

Week 2	Unit 2 (Standard Course)			4-Day
Weekly Topic				
➔ This week will look at covalent bonding.				
	Day 1	Day 2	Day 3	Day 4
Textbook and Experiment	❒ Read *CK-12 Chemistry* Sections 9.1 and 9.2.	❒ Read *CK-12 Chemistry* Sections 9.3 and 9.4.	❒ Read the background and procedure sections for the week's lab.	❒ Do the "Observe a Decompostion Reaction" lab on pg. 60 in *The Home Scientist Chemistry Laboratory Manual.* **OR** ❒ Do the online lab "Atomic Emission Spectra."
Writing	❒ Add the vocabulary to the glossary section of your science notebook.	❒ Answer the assigned questions in the reading section of your science notebook.	❒ Take the Chapter 8 Test from *CK-12 Chemistry.*	❒ Record what you have done in the lab section of your science notebook.
Other Notes				

Week 2	Unit 2 (Survey Course)	2-Day
Weekly Topic		
➔ This week will look at covalent bonding.		
	Day 1	**Day 2**
Textbook	❒ Read *CK-12 Chemistry* Sections 9.1 and 9.2.	❒ Read *CK-12 Chemistry* Sections 9.3 and 9.4.
Writing	❒ Add the vocabulary to the glossary section of your science notebook. ❒ Take the Chapter 8 Test from *CK-12 Chemistry*.	❒ Answer the assigned questions in the reading section of your science notebook.
Events in Science	❒ Choose one of the Events in Science assignments to do and add your work to the events section of your science notebook.	
Other Notes		

Week 3 Notes - The Mole

Textbook Assignments

Reading

📖 *CK-12 Chemistry* Section 10.1, 10.2, 10.3

Written

After you finish reading, answer questions #1-6 in section 10.1, #1-4 in section 10.2, and #5-7 in 10.3 and file your work in the reading section of your science notebook. Then, define the following terms in the glossary section of your science notebook:

- ☐ Avogadro's Number
- ☐ Mole
- ☐ STP
- ☐ Molar Volume
- ☐ Representative Particle

Experiment - Observe Electrolysis

Purpose

The purpose of this lab is to observe and explain how electrolysis works.

Pre-Reading

- Read the background and procedure sections for the "Observe Electrolysis" lab on pg. 146 in *The Home Scientist Chemistry Laboratory Manual.*

Procedure

- ✓ Do the lab entitled "Observe Electrolysis" on pg. 146 in *The Home Scientist Chemistry Laboratory Manual.*

Lab Notebook

- ☞ Write down on a sheet of paper or type out your notes as you do the experiment. After you are done, print out your lab notes and add them to the lab section of your science notebook.

Lab Questions

- Complete the multiple choice section of the "Observe Electrolysis" lab on pg. 149 in *The Home Scientist Chemistry Laboratory Manual.* Record the answers in the lab section of your science notebook.

Online Lab - Lab 11: Pressure-Volume Relationship for Gases

Purpose

The purpose of this online lab is to investigate the relationship between the pressure and volume of a gas.

Pre-Reading

- Print and read the section of the workbook for the "Pressure-Volume Relationship for Gases" online lab.

Procedure

- ✓ Do the lab entitled "Pressure-Volume Relationship for Gases" and answer the questions as you work through the online lab.

Lab Notebook

- ☞ Add the completed workbook pages that were printed to the lab notebook.

Events in Science

Current Events

- 🕒 Find a current events article relating to the field of molecular chemistry and complete the article summary sheet found on pg. 245 of the Appendix. Once you are done, add the sheet to the events section of your science notebook.

Historical Figures

- 🕒 Continue to research the life and work of Neils Bohr.

Hands-on Activity

Optional Hands-on

- ✂ Celebrate Avogadro's number by having your own mole day! See the following website for ideas of activities you could do: http://www.moleday.org/.

Week 3 Supply List

Weekly Experiment	
Supplies from CK01B Chemistry Kit	❒ Goggles, Battery 9V, Battery adapter, Beaker-250 mL, Graduated cylinder-10 mL, Magnesium sulfate, Spatula, Stirring rod, Stoppers, Test tubes-glass, Wood splints
Additional Supplies From Home	❒ Gloves, Butane lighter (or other flame source), Rubber band, Digital multimeter (optional), Water-distilled
Hands-on Activity	
Supplies Needed	❒ Supplies will vary based on the activities you choose to do.

Week 3	Unit 2 (Honors Course)				5-Day
Weekly Topic					
➔ This week will look at unit of measurement, the mole.					
	Day 1	Day 2	Day 3	Day 4	Day 5
Textbook and Experiment	❐ Read *CK-12 Chemistry* Sections 10.1 and 10.2.	❐ Read *CK-12 Chemistry* Section 10.3.	❐ Read the background and procedure sections for the week's lab.	❐ Do the "Observe Electrolysis" lab on pg. 146 in *The Home Scientist Chemistry Laboratory Manual.*	❐ Do the optional Hands-on Assignment - Units of Measurement.
Writing	❐ Add the vocabulary to the glossary section of your science notebook.	❐ Answer the assigned questions in the reading section of your science notebook.	❐ Take the Chapter 9 Test from *CK-12 Chemistry.*	❐ Record what you have done in the lab section of your science notebook.	❐ Complete the lab review questions for the week.
Events in Science	❐ Choose one of the Events in Science assignments to do and add your work to the events section of your science notebook.				
Other Notes					

Week 3	Unit 2 (Standard Course)			4-Day
Weekly Topic				
➔ This week will look at unit of measurement, the mole.				
	Day 1	Day 2	Day 3	Day 4
Textbook and Experiment	❒ Read *CK-12 Chemistry* Sections 10.1 and 10.2.	❒ Read *CK-12 Chemistry* Section 10.3.	❒ Read the background and procedure sections for the week's lab.	❒ Do the "Observe Electrolysis" lab on pg. 146 in *The Home Scientist Chemistry Laboratory Manual.* **OR** ❒ Do the online lab "Pressure-Volume Relationship for Gases."
Writing	❒ Add the vocabulary to the glossary section of your science notebook.	❒ Answer the assigned questions in the reading section of your science notebook.	❒ Take the Chapter 9 Test from *CK-12 Chemistry.*	❒ Record what you have done in the lab section of your science notebook.
Other Notes				

Week 3	Unit 2 (Survey Course)	2-Day
Weekly Topic		
➔ This week will look at unit of measurement, the mole.		
	Day 1	**Day 2**
Textbook	❒ Read *CK-12 Chemistry* Sections 10.1 and 10.2.	❒ Read *CK-12 Chemistry* Section 10.3.
Writing	❒ Add the vocabulary to the glossary section of your science notebook. ❒ Take the Chapter 9 Test from *CK-12 Chemistry.*	❒ Answer the assigned questions in the reading section of your science notebook.
Events in Science	❒ Choose one of the Events in Science assignments to do and add your work to the events section of your science notebook.	
Other Notes		

Week 4 Notes - Chemical Reactions

Textbook Assignments

Reading

📖 *CK-12 Chemistry* Sections 11.1, 11.2

📖 Written

After you finish reading, answer questions #1-6 in section 11.1 and #1-6 in section 11.2 and file your work in the reading section of your science notebook. Then, define the following terms in the glossary section of your science notebook:

- ☐ Balanced Equations
- ☐ Chemical Equations
- ☐ Coefficient
- ☐ Decomposition
- ☐ Activity Series
- ☐ Single Replacement Reaction
- ☐ Double Replacement Reaction

Experiment - Observe the Electrochemical Oxidation of Iron

Purpose

The purpose of this lab is to describe and observe the electrochemical oxidation of iron.

Pre-Reading

Read the background and procedure sections for the "Observe the Electrochemical Oxidation of Iron" lab on pg. 150 in *The Home Scientist Chemistry Laboratory Manual.*

Procedure

✓ Do the lab entitled "Observe the Electrochemical Oxidation of Iron" on pg. 150 in *The Home Scientist Chemistry Laboratory Manual.*

Lab Notebook

Write down on a sheet of paper or type out your notes as you do the experiment. After you are done, print out your lab notes and add them to the lab section of your science notebook.

Lab Questions

Complete the multiple choice section of the "Observe the Electrochemical Oxidation of Iron" lab on pg. 155 in *The Home Scientist Chemistry Laboratory Manual.* Record the answers in the lab section of your science notebook.

Online Lab - Lab 12: Temperature-Volume Relationship for Gases

Purpose

The purpose of this online lab is to investigate the relationship between the temperature and volume of a gas.

Pre-Reading

Print and read the section of the workbook for the "Temperature-Volume Relationship for Gases" online lab.

Procedure

✓ Do the lab entitled "Temperature-Volume Relationship for Gases" and answer the questions as you work through the online lab.

Lab Notebook

☞ Add the completed workbook pages that were printed to the lab notebook.

Events in Science

Current Events

🕒 Find a current events article relating to the field of molecular chemistry and complete the article summary sheet found on pg. 245 of the Appendix. Once you are done, add the sheet to the events section of your science notebook.

Historical Figures

🕒 Continue to research the life and work of Neils Bohr.

Hands-on Activity

Optional Hands-on

✂ Watch a chemical reaction in your kitchen! You will need baking soda, white vinegar, and a cup. Add a quarter of a cup of vinegar to the cup. Then, sprinkle about a tablespoon of baking soda into the cup and observe what happens. (*This is a classic example of a chemical reaction. Sodium bicarbonate (baking soda) reacts with acetic acid and water (vinegar) to release carbon dioxide (the bubbles you saw) and forming sodium acetate.)*

Week 4 Supply List

Weekly Experiment	
Supplies from CK01B Chemistry Kit	❒ Goggles, Beaker-250 mL, Centrifuge tubes-15 mL, Iron wool, Sharpie marking pen, Spatula, Test tube rack
Additional Supplies From Home	❒ Gloves, Microwave oven, Sodium chloride (table salt), Water-distilled
Hands-on Activity	
Supplies Needed	❒ Baking soda, White vinegar, Cup

Week 4	Unit 2 (Honors Course)				5-Day
Weekly Topic					
➔ This week will look at chemical reactions.					
	Day 1	Day 2	Day 3	Day 4	Day 5
Textbook and Experiment	❒ Read *CK-12 Chemistry* Section 11.1.	❒ Read *CK-12 Chemistry* Section 11.2.	❒ Read the background and procedure sections for the week's lab.	❒ Do the "Observe the Electrochemical Oxidation of Iron" lab on pg. 150 in *The Home Scientist Chemistry Laboratory Manual*.	❒ Do the optional Hands-on Assignment - Density Column.
Writing	❒ Add the vocabulary to the glossary section of your science notebook.	❒ Answer the assigned questions in the reading section of your science notebook.	❒ Take the Chapter 10 Test from *CK-12 Chemistry*.	❒ Record what you have done in the lab section of your science notebook.	❒ Complete the lab review questions for the week.
Events in Science	❒ Choose one of the Events in Science assignments to do and add your work to the events section of your science notebook.				
Other Notes					

Week 4	Unit 2 (Standard Course)			4-Day
Weekly Topic				
➔ This week will look at chemical reactions.				
	Day 1	Day 2	Day 3	Day 4
Textbook and Experiment	❒ Read *CK-12 Chemistry* Section 11.1.	❒ Read *CK-12 Chemistry* Sections 11.2.	❒ Read the background and procedure sections for the week's lab.	❒ Do the "Observe the Electrochemical Oxidation of Iron" lab on pg. 150 in *The Home Scientist Chemistry Laboratory Manual*. **OR** ❒ Do the online lab "Temperature-Volume Relationship for Gases."
Writing	❒ Add the vocabulary to the glossary section of your science notebook.	❒ Answer the assigned questions in the reading section of your science notebook.	❒ Take the Chapter 10 Test from *CK-12 Chemistry*.	❒ Record what you have done in the lab section of your science notebook.
Other Notes				

Week 4	Unit 2 (Survey Course)	2-Day
	Weekly Topic	
➔ This week will look at chemical reactions.		
	Day 1	**Day 2**
Textbook	❐ Read *CK-12 Chemistry* Section 11.1.	❐ Read *CK-12 Chemistry* Sections 11.2.
Writing	❐ Add the vocabulary to the glossary section of your science notebook. ❐ Take the Chapter 10 Test from *CK-12 Chemistry.*	❐ Answer the assigned questions in the reading section of your science notebook.
Events in Science	❐ Choose one of the Events in Science assignments to do and add your work to the events section of your science notebook.	
	Other Notes	

Week 5 Notes - Stoichiometry

Textbook Assignments

Reading

📖 *CK-12 Chemistry* Sections 12.1, 12.2, 12.3

Written

After you finish reading, answer questions #1,3,5 in section 12.1, questions #1-5 in section 12.2, and questions #4-7 in section 12.3. File your work in the reading section of your science notebook. Then, define the following terms in the glossary section of your science notebook:

- ☐ Mole Ratio
- ☐ Stoichiometry
- ☐ Actual Yield
- ☐ Excess Reagent
- ☐ Limiting Reagent
- ☐ Theoretical Yield

Experiment - Observe a Single Replacement Reaction

Purpose

The purpose of this lab is to observe a single replacement reaction.

Pre-Reading

- Read the background and procedure sections for the "Observe a Single Replacement Reaction" lab on pg. 63 in *The Home Scientist Chemistry Laboratory Manual.*

Procedure

- ✓ Do the lab entitled "Observe a Single Replacement Reaction" on pg. 63 in *The Home Scientist Chemistry Laboratory Manual.*

Lab Notebook

- Write down on a sheet of paper or type out your notes as you do the experiment. After you are done, print out your lab notes and add them to the lab section of your science notebook.

Lab Questions

- Complete the multiple choice section of the "Observe a Single Replacement Reaction" lab on pg. 64 in *The Home Scientist Chemistry Laboratory Manual.* Record the answers in the lab section of your science notebook.

Online Lab - Lab 13: Derivation of the Ideal Gas Law

Purpose

The purpose of this online lab is to derive the Ideal Gas Law from experimentally and to find the value of the Universal Gas Constant (R).

Pre-Reading

- Print and read the section of the workbook for the "Derivation of the Ideal Gas Law" online lab.

Procedure

- ✓ Do the lab entitled "Derivation of the Ideal Gas Law" and answer the questions as you work through the online lab.

Lab Notebook

- ☞ Add the completed workbook pages that were printed to the lab notebook.

Events in Science

Current Events

- 🕒 Find a current events article relating to the field of molecular chemistry and complete the article summary sheet found on pg. 245 of the Appendix. Once you are done, add the sheet to the events section of your science notebook.

Historical Figures

- 🕒 Continue to research the life and work of Neils Bohr.

Hands-on Activity

Optional Hands-on

- ✂ Play around with the Phet simulation for reactants, products, and leftovers found here: https://phet.colorado.edu/en/simulation/reactants-products-and-leftovers.

Week 5 Supply List

Weekly Experiment	
Supplies from CK01B Chemistry Kit	❒ Goggles, Pipettes, Reaction plate 24-well, Reaction plate 96-well, Copper(II) sulfate solution, Iron wool, Potassium ferricyanide solution
Additional Supplies From Home	❒ Gloves, Paper-white
Hands-on Activity	
Supplies Needed	❒ None

Week 5	Unit 2 (Honors Course)				5-Day
Weekly Topic					
➔ This week will look at stoichiometry.					
	Day 1	Day 2	Day 3	Day 4	Day 5
Textbook and Experiment	❒ Read *CK-12 Chemistry* Sections 12.1 and 12.2.	❒ Read *CK-12 Chemistry* Section 12.3.	❒ Read the background and procedure sections for the week's lab.	❒ Do the "Observe a Single Replacement Reaction" lab on pg. 63 in *The Home Scientist Chemistry Laboratory Manual.*	❒ Do the optional Hands-on Assignment - Phet Reaction Simulation.
Writing	❒ Add the vocabulary to the glossary section of your science notebook.	❒ Answer the assigned questions in the reading section of your science notebook.	❒ Take the Chapter 11 Test from *CK-12 Chemistry.*	❒ Record what you have done in the lab section of your science notebook.	❒ Complete the lab review questions for the week.
Events in Science	❒ Choose one of the Events in Science assignments to do and add your work to the events section of your science notebook.				
Other Notes					

Week 5	Unit 2 (Standard Course)			4-Day
Weekly Topic				
➔ This week will look at stoichiometry.				
	Day 1	Day 2	Day 3	Day 4
Textbook and Experiment	❒ Read *CK-12 Chemistry* Sections 12.1 and 12.2.	❒ Read *CK-12 Chemistry* Section 12.3.	❒ Read the background and procedure sections for the week's lab.	❒ Do the "Observe a Single Replacement Reaction" lab on pg. 63 in *The Home Scientist Chemistry Laboratory Manual.* **OR** ❒ Do the online lab "Derivation of the Ideal Gas Law."
Writing	❒ Add the vocabulary to the glossary section of your science notebook.	❒ Answer the assigned questions in the reading section of your science notebook.	❒ Take the Chapter 11 Test from *CK-12 Chemistry.*	❒ Record what you have done in the lab section of your science notebook.
Other Notes				

Week 5	Unit 2 (Survey Course)	2-Day
Weekly Topic		
➔ This week will look at stoichiometry.		
	Day 1	**Day 2**
Textbook	❒ Read *CK-12 Chemistry* Sections 12.1 and 12.2.	❒ Read *CK-12 Chemistry* Section 12.3.
Writing	❒ Add the vocabulary to the glossary section of your science notebook. ❒ Take the Chapter 11 Test from *CK-12 Chemistry*.	❒ Answer the assigned questions in the reading section of your science notebook.
Events in Science	❒ Choose one of the Events in Science assignments to do and add your work to the events section of your science notebook.	
Other Notes		

Week 6 Notes - States of Matter, Part 1

Textbook Assignments

Reading

📖 *CK-12 Chemistry* Section 13.1, 13.2

Written

After you finish reading, answer questions #1-4,8 in section 13.1, and #1-6 in section 13.2. File your work in the reading section of your science notebook. Then, define the following terms in the glossary section of your science notebook:

- ☐ Barometer
- ☐ Pascal
- ☐ Pressure
- ☐ Ideal Gas
- ☐ Condensation
- ☐ Vapor Pressure
- ☐ Surface Tension

Experiment - Observe a Double Replacement Reaction

Purpose

The purpose of this lab is to explain and observe observe a double replacement reaction

Pre-Reading

Read the background and procedure sections for the "Observe a Double Replacement Reaction" lab on pg. 65 in *The Home Scientist Chemistry Laboratory Manual.*

Procedure

✓ Do the lab entitled "Observe a Double Replacement Reaction" on pg. 65 in *The Home Scientist Chemistry Laboratory Manual.*

Lab Notebook

☞ Write down on a sheet of paper or type out your notes as you do the experiment. After you are done, print out your lab notes and add them to the lab section of your science notebook.

Lab Questions

Complete the multiple choice section of the "Observe a Double Replacement Reaction" lab on pg. 69 in *The Home Scientist Chemistry Laboratory Manual.* Record the answers in the lab section of your science notebook.

Online Lab - Lab 14: Ideal vs. Real Gases

Purpose

The purpose of this online lab is to dinvestigate how temperature and pressure changes affect ideal and real gases.

Pre-Reading

Print and read the section of the workbook for the "Ideal vs. Real Gases" online lab.

Procedure

- ✓ Do the lab entitled "Ideal vs. Real Gases" and answer the questions as you work through the online lab.

Lab Notebook

- ☞ Add the completed workbook pages that were printed to the lab notebook.

Events in Science

Current Events

- 🕒 Find a current events article relating to the field of molecular chemistry and complete the article summary sheet found on pg. 245 of the Appendix. Once you are done, add the sheet to the events section of your science notebook.

Historical Figures

- 🕒 Begin to work on your paper on the life and work of Neils Bohr. This week, aim to complete your outline. See pg. 14 for more directions. You will have three weeks to complete this paper.

Hands-on Activity

Optional Hands-on

- ✂ Explore the surface tension of water using a penny, some water, and an eye dropper. Lay the penny on a flat surface. Then, use the eyedropper to slowly add five to six drops of water to the top of the penny. Observe what happens. (*You should see a dome of water form on top of the penny.*)

Week 6 Supply List

Weekly Experiment	
Supplies from CK01B Chemistry Kit	❒ Goggles, Beakers, Pipettes, Reaction plates 24-well and 96-well, Spatula, Barium nitrate-0.1M, Calcium nitrate-0.1M, Copper(II) sulfate-1M, Lead(II) acetate-0.1M, Hydrochloric acid-6M, Magnesium sulfate, Potassium dichromate-0.1M, Potassium ferricyanide-0.1M, Potassium iodide-0.1M, Sodium hydroxide-6M, Sodium oxalate-0.1M, Sodium sulfide-0.1M
Additional Supplies From Home	❒ Gloves, Desk lamp or other strong light source, Sheets of white and black paper, Distilled water
Hands-on Activity	
Supplies Needed	❒ Penny, Water, Eye dropper

Week 6	Unit 2 (Honors Course)				5-Day
Weekly Topic					
➔ This week will begin a look at states of matter.					
	Day 1	Day 2	Day 3	Day 4	Day 5
Textbook and Experiment	❒ Read *CK-12 Chemistry* Section 13.1.	❒ Read *CK-12 Chemistry* Section 13.2.	❒ Read the background and procedure sections for the week's lab.	❒ Do the "Observe a Double Replacement Reaction" lab on pg. 65 in *The Home Scientist Chemistry Laboratory Manual.*	❒ Do the optional Hands-on Assignment - Surface Tension.
Writing	❒ Add the vocabulary to the glossary section of your science notebook.	❒ Answer the assigned questions in the reading section of your science notebook.	❒ Take the Chapter 12 Test from *CK-12 Chemistry.*	❒ Record what you have done in the lab section of your science notebook.	❒ Complete the lab review questions for the week.
Events in Science	❒ Choose one of the Events in Science assignments to do and add your work to the events section of your science notebook.				
Other Notes					

Week 6	Unit 2 (Standard Course)			4-Day
Weekly Topic				
➔ This week will begin a look at states of matter.				
	Day 1	Day 2	Day 3	Day 4
Textbook and Experiment	❒ Read *CK-12 Chemistry* Section 13.1.	❒ Read *CK-12 Chemistry* Section 13.2.	❒ Read the background and procedure sections for the week's lab.	❒ Do the "Observe a Double Replacement Reaction" lab on pg. 65 in *The Home Scientist Chemistry Laboratory Manual.* **OR** ❒ Do the online lab "Ideal vs. Real Gases."
Writing	❒ Add the vocabulary to the glossary section of your science notebook.	❒ Answer the assigned questions in the reading section of your science notebook.	❒ Take the Chapter 12 Test from *CK-12 Chemistry.*	❒ Record what you have done in the lab section of your science notebook.
Other Notes				

Week 6	Unit 2 (Survey Course)	2-Day
Weekly Topic		
➔ This week will begin a look at states of matter.		
	Day 1	Day 2
Textbook	❒ Read *CK-12 Chemistry* Section 13.1.	❒ Read *CK-12 Chemistry* Section 13.2.
Writing	❒ Add the vocabulary to the glossary section of your science notebook. ❒ Take the Chapter 12 Test from *CK-12 Chemistry*.	❒ Answer the assigned questions in the reading section of your science notebook.
Events in Science	❒ Choose one of the Events in Science assignments to do and add your work to the events section of your science notebook.	
Other Notes		

Week 7 Notes - States of Matter, part 2

Textbook Assignments

Reading

📖 *CK-12 Chemistry* Sections 13.3, 13.4

Written

After you finish reading, answer questions #1-7 in section 13.3 and question #7 in section 13.4. File your work in the reading section of your science notebook. Then, define the following terms in the glossary section of your science notebook:

- ☐ Amorphous Solid
- ☐ Sublimation
- ☐ Decomposition
- ☐ Critical Pressure
- ☐ Triple Point
- ☐ Phase Diagram

Experiment - Stoichometry of a Double Replacement Reaction

Purpose

The purpose of this lab is to learn the concepts of Stoichometry and observe the Stoichometry of a double replacement reaction.

Pre-Reading

Read the background and procedure sections for the "Stoichometry of a Double Replacement Reaction" lab on pg. 70 in *The Home Scientist Chemistry Laboratory Manual.*

Procedure

✓ Do the lab entitled "Stoichometry of a Double Replacement Reaction" on pg. 70 in *The Home Scientist Chemistry Laboratory Manual.*

Lab Notebook

☞ Write down on a sheet of paper or type out your notes as you do the experiment. After you are done, print out your lab notes and add them to the lab section of your science notebook.

Lab Questions

Complete the multiple choice section of the "Stoichometry of a Double Replacement Reaction" lab on pg. 72 in *The Home Scientist Chemistry Laboratory Manual.* Record the answers in the lab section of your science notebook.

Online Lab - Lab 15: Investigation of Gas Pressure and Mass

Purpose

The purpose of this online lab is to investigate the relationship between the internal pressure of a gas and the applied external pressure by placing weights on a frictionless massless piston.

Pre-Reading

Print and read the section of the workbook for the "Investigation of Gas Pressure and

Mass" online lab.

Procedure

✓ Do the lab entitled "Investigation of Gas Pressure and Mass" and answer the questions as you work through the online lab.

Lab Notebook

☞ Add the completed workbook pages that were printed to the lab notebook.

Events in Science

Current Events

🕒 Find a current events article relating to the field of molecular chemistry and complete the article summary sheet found on pg. 245 of the Appendix. Once you are done, add the sheet to the events section of your science notebook.

Historical Figures

🕒 Continue work on your paper on the life and work of Neils Bohr. This week, aim to complete your rough draft. See pg. 14 for more directions.

Hands-on Activity

Optional Hands-on

✂ Play with dry ice, which sublimes easily at room temperature. Here are a few ideas for exploring dry ice: http://elementalblogging.com/dry-ice-exploration/. For the three activities suggested in the post, you will need dry ice, a cup, water, dish soap, and two plates.

Week 7 Supply List

Weekly Experiment	
Supplies from CK01B Chemistry Kit	❒ Goggles, Pipettes, Reaction plate 24-well, Lead(II) acetate-0.1M, Potassium dichromate-0.1M, Potassium iodide-0.1M
Additional Supplies From Home	❒ Gloves, Distilled water
Hands-on Activity	
Supplies Needed	❒ Dry ice, Cup, Water, Dish soap, 2 Plates

Week 7	Unit 2 (Honors Course)				5-Day
Weekly Topic					
➔ This week will wrap up a look at states of matter.					
	Day 1	Day 2	Day 3	Day 4	Day 5
Textbook and Experiment	❒ Read *CK-12 Chemistry* Section 13.3.	❒ Read *CK-12 Chemistry* Section 13.4.	❒ Read the background and procedure sections for the week's lab.	❒ Do the "Stoichometry of a Double Replacement Reaction" lab on pg. 70 in *The Home Scientist Chemistry Laboratory Manual.*	❒ Do the optional Hands-on Assignment - Dry Ice.
Writing	❒ Add the vocabulary to the glossary section of your science notebook.	❒ Answer the assigned questions in the reading section of your science notebook.		❒ Record what you have done in the lab section of your science notebook.	❒ Complete the lab review questions for the week.
Events in Science	❒ Choose one of the Events in Science assignments to do and add your work to the events section of your science notebook.				
Other Notes					

Week 7	Unit 2 (Standard Course)			4-Day
Weekly Topic				
➔ This week will wrap up a look at states of matter.				
	Day 1	Day 2	Day 3	Day 4
Textbook and Experiment	❒ Read *CK-12 Chemistry* Section 13.3.	❒ Read *CK-12 Chemistry* Section 13.4.	❒ Read the background and procedure sections for the week's lab.	❒ Do the "Stoichometry of a Double Replacement Reaction" lab on pg. 70 in *The Home Scientist Chemistry Laboratory Manual.* **OR** ❒ Do the online lab "Investigation of Gas Pressure and Mass."
Writing	❒ Add the vocabulary to the glossary section of your science notebook.	❒ Answer the assigned questions in the reading section of your science notebook.		❒ Record what you have done in the lab section of your science notebook.
Other Notes				

Week 7	Unit 2 (Survey Course)	2-Day
Weekly Topic		
➔ This week will wrap up a look at states of matter.		
	Day 1	Day 2
Textbook	❒ Read *CK-12 Chemistry* Section 13.3.	❒ Read *CK-12 Chemistry* Section 13.4.
Writing	❒ Add the vocabulary to the glossary section of your science notebook.	❒ Answer the assigned questions in the reading section of your science notebook.
Events in Science	❒ Choose one of the Events in Science assignments to do and add your work to the events section of your science notebook.	
Other Notes		

Week 8 Notes - Behavior of Gases, part 1

Textbook Assignments

Reading

📖 *CK-12 Chemistry* Section 14.1, 14.2

Written

After you finish reading, answer questions #1-7 in section 14.1 and #1-5 in section 14.2 and file your work in the reading section of your science notebook. Then, define the following terms in the glossary section of your science notebook:

- ☐ Compressibility
- ☐ Atomic Mass Unit
- ☐ Avogadro's Law
- ☐ Boyle's Law
- ☐ Charles's Law
- ☐ Gay-Lussac's Law

Experiment - Observe the Pressure-Volume Relationship of Gases (Boyle's Law)

Purpose

The purpose of this lab is to explain the relationship between volume and the pressure of an ideal gas.

Pre-Reading

Read the background and procedure sections for the "Observe the Pressure-Volume Relationship of Gases (Boyle's Law)" lab on pg. 124 in *The Home Scientist Chemistry Laboratory Manual.*

Procedure

✓ Do the lab entitled "Observe the Pressure-Volume Relationship of Gases (Boyle's Law)" on pg. 124 in *The Home Scientist Chemistry Laboratory Manual.*

Lab Notebook

☞ Write down on a sheet of paper or type out your notes as you do the experiment. After you are done, print out your lab notes and add them to the lab section of your science notebook.

Lab Questions

Complete the multiple choice section of the "Observe the Pressure-Volume Relationship of Gases (Boyle's Law)" lab on pg. 126 in *The Home Scientist Chemistry Laboratory Manual.* Record the answers in the lab section of your science notebook.

Online Lab - Lab 8: Photoelectric Effect

Purpose

The purpose of this online lab is to duplicate the photoelectric effect experiments.

Pre-Reading

- Print and read the section of the workbook for the "Photoelectric Effect" online lab.

Procedure

- ✓ Do the lab entitled "Photoelectric Effect" and answer the questions as you work through the online lab.

Lab Notebook

- Add the completed workbook pages that were printed to the lab notebook.

Events in Science

Current Events

- Find a current events article relating to the field of molecular chemistry and complete the article summary sheet found on pg. 245 of the Appendix. Once you are done, add the sheet to the events section of your science notebook.

Historical Figures

- Continue work on your paper on the life and work of Neils Bohr. This week, aim to complete your final draft. See pg. 14 for more directions.

Hands-on Activity

Optional Hands-on

- Test Boyle's Law with a medicine dropper and two mini-marshmallows. Remove the plunger from the medicine dropper and insert two marshmallows. Put the plunger back in, leaving a small pocket of air between the marshmallow stack and the end of the plunger. Place your finger on the tip of the medicine dropper to create a vacuum. Then, pull the plunger up and down to observe what happens to the marshmallows. (*You should see them expand as you pull the plunger up and shrink as you push it down.*)

Week 8 Supply List

Weekly Experiment	
Supplies from CK01B Chemistry Kit	❒ Goggles, Beakers - 250 mL, 100 mL, 50 mL, Cylinder, graduated - 10 mL, Syringe - 10 mL
Additional Supplies From Home	❒ Gloves, Soda bottle (2-liter, clean and empty), Vegetable oil
Hands-on Activity	
Supplies Needed	❒ Medicine dropper, 2 Mini-marshmallows

Week 8	Unit 2 (Honors Course)				5-Day
Weekly Topic					
➔ This week will begin a look at the behavior of gases.					
	Day 1	Day 2	Day 3	Day 4	Day 5
Textbook and Experiment	❒ Read *CK-12 Chemistry* Section 14.1.	❒ Read *CK-12 Chemistry* Section 14.2.	❒ Read the background and procedure sections for the week's lab.	❒ Do the "Observe the Pressure-Volume Relationship of Gases (Boyle's Law)" lab on pg. 124 in *The Home Scientist Chemistry Laboratory Manual.*	❒ Do the optional Hands-on Assignment - Boyle's Law.
Writing	❒ Add the vocabulary to the glossary section of your science notebook.	❒ Answer the assigned questions in the reading section of your science notebook.	❒ Take the Chapter 13 Test from *CK-12 Chemistry.*	❒ Record what you have done in the lab section of your science notebook.	❒ Complete the lab review questions for the week.
Events in Science	❒ Choose one of the Events in Science assignments to do and add your work to the events section of your science notebook.				
Other Notes					

Week 8	Unit 2 (Standard Course)			4-Day
Weekly Topic				
➔ This week will begin a look at the behavior of gases.				
	Day 1	Day 2	Day 3	Day 4
Textbook and Experiment	❒ Read *CK-12 Chemistry* Section 14.1.	❒ Read *CK-12 Chemistry* Section 14.2.	❒ Read the background and procedure sections for the week's lab.	❒ Do the "Observe the Pressure-Volume Relationship of Gases (Boyle's Law)" lab on pg. 124 in *The Home Scientist Chemistry Laboratory Manual*. **OR** ❒ Do the online lab "Photoelectric Effect."
Writing	❒ Add the vocabulary to the glossary section of your science notebook.	❒ Answer the assigned questions in the reading section of your science notebook.	❒ Take the Chapter 13 Test from *CK-12 Chemistry*.	❒ Record what you have done in the lab section of your science notebook.
Other Notes				

Week 8	Unit 2 (Survey Course)	2-Day
Weekly Topic		
➔ This week will begin a look at the behavior of gases.		
	Day 1	**Day 2**
Textbook	❒ Read *CK-12 Chemistry* Section 14.1.	❒ Read *CK-12 Chemistry* Section 14.2.
Writing	❒ Add the vocabulary to the glossary section of your science notebook. ❒ Take the Chapter 13 Test from *CK-12 Chemistry.*	❒ Answer the assigned questions in the reading section of your science notebook.
Events in Science	❒ Choose one of the Events in Science assignments to do and add your work to the events section of your science notebook.	
Other Notes		

Week 9 Notes - Behavior of Gases, part 2

Textbook Assignments

Reading

📖 *CK-12 Chemistry* Sections 14.3, 14.4

Written

After you finish reading, answer questions #1-10 in section 14.3 and questions #1-7 in 14.4. File your work in the reading section of your science notebook. Then, define the following terms in the glossary section of your science notebook:

- ☐ Ideal Gas Constant
- ☐ Ideal Gas Law
- ☐ Constant
- ☐ Dalton's Law Of Partial Pressures
- ☐ Effusion
- ☐ Partial Pressure
- ☐ Mole Fraction

Experiment - Observe the Volume-Temperature Relationship of Gases (Charles's Law)

Purpose

The purpose of this lab is to explain the relationship between volume and the pressure of an ideal gas.

Pre-Reading

👓 Read the background and procedure sections for the "Observe the Volume-Temperature Relationship of Gases (Charles's Law)" lab on pg. 128 in *The Home Scientist Chemistry Laboratory Manual.*

Procedure

✓ Do the lab entitled "Observe the Volume-Temperature Relationship of Gases (Charles's Law)" on pg. 128 in *The Home Scientist Chemistry Laboratory Manual.*

Lab Notebook

☞ Write down on a sheet of paper or type out your notes as you do the experiment. After you are done, print out your lab notes and add them to the lab section of your science notebook.

Lab Questions

Complete the multiple choice section of the "Observe the Volume-Temperature Relationship of Gases (Charles's Law)" lab on pg. 130 in *The Home Scientist Chemistry Laboratory Manual.* Record the answers in the lab section of your science notebook.

Online Lab

☞ There is no online lab scheduled for this week.

Events in Science

Current Events

🕒 There is no assignment for this week.

Historical Figures

🕒 There is no assignment for this week.

Hands-on Activity

Optional Hands-on

✂ Test Charles's Law with two balloons, a bucket, water, and ice. Blow each of the balloons up to the same size. Place one on the counter and one in a bucket of ice water. Wait for 10 minutes and take the balloon out of the ice water. Compare the two balloons side by side. (*You should see that the one that was in the ice water has decreased in size because, as the temperature decreases, the volume of a gas will also decrease.*)

Week 9 Supply List

Weekly Experiment	
Supplies from CK01B Chemistry Kit	❐ Goggles, Beaker-250 mL, Syringe-10 mL, Thermometer
Additional Supplies From Home	❐ Gloves, Freezer, Microwave oven, Ice, Vegetable oil
Hands-on Activity	
Supplies Needed	❐ Sample liquids (oil, fruit juice, water, saltwater, and so on), Ice cube tray, Instant thermometer

Week 9	Unit 2 (Honors Course)				5-Day
Weekly Topic					
➔ This week will wrap up a look at the behavior of gases.					
	Day 1	Day 2	Day 3	Day 4	Day 5
Textbook and Experiment	❒ Read *CK-12 Chemistry* Section 14.1.	❒ Read *CK-12 Chemistry* Section 14.2.	❒ Read the background and procedure sections for the week's lab.	❒ Do the "Observe the Volume-Temperature Relationship of Gases (Charles's Law)" lab on pg. 128 in *The Home Scientist Chemistry Laboratory Manual.*	❒ Do the optional Hands-on Assignment - Charles' Law.
Writing	❒ Add the vocabulary to the glossary section of your science notebook.	❒ Answer the assigned questions in the reading section of your science notebook.	❒ Take the Chapter 14 Test from *CK-12 Chemistry.*	❒ Record what you have done in the lab section of your science notebook.	❒ Complete the lab review questions for the week.
Other Notes					

Week 9	Unit 2 (Standard Course)			4-Day
Weekly Topic				
➔ This week will wrap up a look at the behavior of gases.				
	Day 1	Day 2	Day 3	Day 4
Textbook and Experiment	❒ Read *CK-12 Chemistry* Section 14.1.	❒ Read *CK-12 Chemistry* Section 14.2.	❒ Read the background and procedure sections for the week's lab.	❒ Do the "Observe the Volume-Temperature Relationship of Gases (Charles's Law)" lab on pg. 128 in *The Home Scientist Chemistry Laboratory Manual.*
Writing	❒ Add the vocabulary to the glossary section of your science notebook.	❒ Answer the assigned questions in the reading section of your science notebook.	❒ Take the Chapter 14 Test from *CK-12 Chemistry.*	❒ Record what you have done in the lab section of your science notebook.
Other Notes				

Week 9	Unit 2 (Survey Course)	2-Day
Weekly Topic		
➔ This week will wrap up a look at the behavior of gases.		
	Day 1	Day 2
Textbook	❒ Read *CK-12 Chemistry* Section 14.3.	❒ Read *CK-12 Chemistry* Section 14.4.
Writing	❒ Add the vocabulary to the glossary section of your science notebook.	❒ Answer the assigned questions in the reading section of your science notebook.
Other Notes		

Chemistry for High School

Unit 3 - Water and Equilibrium

Week 1 Notes - Water

Textbook Assignments

Reading

🕮 *CK-12 Chemistry* Sections 15.1,15.2,15.3

Written

After you finish reading, answer questions #4-7 in section 15.1 and #6-9 in section 15.2, and #4-7 in section 15.3 and file your work in the reading section of your science notebook. Then, define the following terms in the glossary section of your science notebook:

- ☐ Aqueous Solution
- ☐ Dissociation
- ☐ Immiscible
- ☐ Solute
- ☐ Solvent
- ☐ Strong Electrolyte
- ☐ Colloid
- ☐ Emulsion
- ☐ Suspension
- ☐ Tyndall Effect

Experiment - Observe the Characteristics of a Buffer Solution

Purpose

The purpose of this lab is to observe and explain the characteristics of a buffer solution.

Pre-Reading

Read the background and procedure sections for the "Observe the Characteristics of a Buffer Solution" lab on pg. 117 in *The Home Scientist Chemistry Laboratory Manual.*

Procedure

✓ Do the lab entitled "Observe the Characteristics of a Buffer Solution" on pg. 117 in *The Home Scientist Chemistry Laboratory Manual.*

Lab Notebook

☞ Write down on a sheet of paper or type out your notes as you do the experiment. After you are done, print out your lab notes and add them to the lab section of your science notebook.

Lab Questions

Complete the multiple choice section of the "Observe the Characteristics of a Buffer Solution" lab on pg. 120 in *The Home Scientist Chemistry Laboratory Manual.* Record the answers in the lab section of your science notebook.

Online Lab - Lab 22: Precipitation Reactions - Formation of Solids

Purpose

The purpose of this online lab is to observe, identify, and write balanced equations for precipitation reactions.

Pre-Reading

Print and read the section of the workbook for the "Precipitation Reactions - Formation of Solids" online lab.

Procedure

✓ Do the lab entitled "Precipitation Reactions - Formation of Solids" and answer the questions as you work through the online lab.

Lab Notebook

☞ Add the completed workbook pages that were printed to the lab notebook.

Events in Science

Current Events

🕒 Find a current events article relating to the field of chemistry and complete the article summary sheet found on pg. 245 of the Appendix. Once you are done, add the sheet to the events section of your science notebook.

Historical Figures

🕒 Begin to research the life and work of Robert Boyle, who is responsible for discovering the gas law that relates pressure to volume. You will have four weeks to complete your research. After that, you will have three weeks to prepare a two to three page paper on this scientist and his contributions to the field of chemsitry.

Hands-on Activity

Optional Hands-on

✂ Test the Law of Conservation of Mass using a ziploc baggie, vinegar, baking soda, a paper towel and a scale. Begin by added a half of a cup of vinegar to the baggie. Next, place two tablespoons of baking soda in the center of the paper towel, pull up the corners, and use the rubber band to keep them together. Then, weigh the baggie and the paper towel. Remove them from the scale, add the paper towel bundle to the baggie, and seal the baggie up quickly. Observe the reaction. When it is complete, weigh the baggie once more. (*The weight should be the same.*)

Week 1 Supply List

Weekly Experiment	
Supplies from CK01B Chemistry Kit	❒ Goggles, Acetic acid 6 M, Centrifuge tube 15 mL, Hydrochloric acid 6 M, pH test paper, Pipettes, Reaction plate 24-well, Sodium hydroxide 6 M
Additional Supplies From Home	❒ Gloves, Scissors, Toothpicks plastic, Water (distilled)
Hands-on Activity	
Supplies Needed	❒ Ziploc baggie, Vinegar, Baking soda, Paper towel, Scale

Week 1	Unit 3 (Honors Course)				5-Day
Weekly Topic					
➔ This week will look at the properties of water.					
	Day 1	Day 2	Day 3	Day 4	Day 5
Textbook and Experiment	❒ Read *CK-12 Chemistry* Sections 15.1 and 15.2.	❒ Read *CK-12 Chemistry* Section 15.3.	❒ Read the background and procedure sections for the week's lab.	❒ Do the "Observe the Characteristics of a Buffer Solution" lab on pg. 117 in *The Home Scientist Chemistry Laboratory Manual.*	❒ Do the optional Hands-on Assignment - Conservation of Mass.
Writing	❒ Add the vocabulary to the glossary section of your science notebook.	❒ Answer the assigned questions in the reading section of your science notebook.		❒ Record what you have done in the lab section of your science notebook.	❒ Complete the lab review questions for the week.
Events in Science	❒ Choose one of the Events in Science assignments to do and add your work to the events section of your science notebook.				
Other Notes					

Week 1	Unit 3 (Standard Course)			4-Day
Weekly Topic				
➔ This week will look at the properties of water.				
	Day 1	Day 2	Day 3	Day 4
Textbook and Experiment	❐ Read *CK-12 Chemistry* Sections 15.1 and 15.2.	❐ Read *CK-12 Chemistry* Section 15.3.	❐ Read the background and procedure sections for the week's lab.	❐ Do the "Observe the Characteristics of a Buffer Solution" lab on pg. 117 in *The Home Scientist Chemistry Laboratory Manual.* **OR** ❐ Do the online lab "Precipitation Reactions - Formation of Solids."
Writing	❐ Add the vocabulary to the glossary section of your science notebook.	❐ Answer the assigned questions in the reading section of your science notebook.		❐ Record what you have done in the lab section of your science notebook.
Other Notes				

Week 1	Unit 3 (Survey Course)	2-Day
Weekly Topic		
➔ This week will look at the properties of water.		
	Day 1	Day 2
Textbook	❒ Read *CK-12 Chemistry* Sections 15.1 and 15.2.	❒ Read *CK-12 Chemistry* Section 15.3.
Writing	❒ Add the vocabulary to the glossary section of your science notebook. ❒ Take the Chapter 14 Test from *CK-12 Chemistry.*	❒ Answer the assigned questions in the reading section of your science notebook.
Events in Science	❒ Choose one of the Events in Science assignments to do and add your work to the events section of your science notebook.	
Other Notes		

Week 2 Notes - Solutions, part 1

Textbook Assignments

Reading

📖 *CK-12 Chemistry* Sections 16.1, 16.2

Written

After you finish reading, answer questions #7-9 in section 16.1 and questions #1-7 in section 16.2. File your work in the reading section of your science notebook. Then, define the following terms in the glossary section of your science notebook:

- ☐ Henry's Law
- ☐ Recrystallization
- ☐ Solution Equilibrium
- ☐ Supersaturated Solution
- ☐ Unsaturated Solution
- ☐ Molality
- ☐ Molarity

Experiment - Determine a Solubility Product Constant

Purpose

The purpose of this lab is to explain solvents, solutes, and solubility and to describe the factors that affect solubility.

Pre-Reading

Read the background and procedure sections for the "Determine a Solubility Product Constant" lab on pg. 112 in *The Home Scientist Chemistry Laboratory Manual.*

Procedure

✓ Do the lab entitled "Determine a Solubility Product Constant" on pg. 112 in *The Home Scientist Chemistry Laboratory Manual.*

Lab Notebook

☞ Write down on a sheet of paper or type out your notes as you do the experiment. After you are done, print out your lab notes and add them to the lab section of your science notebook.

Lab Questions

Complete the multiple choice section of the "Determine a Solubility Product Constant" lab on pg. 116 in *The Home Scientist Chemistry Laboratory Manual.* Record the answers in the lab section of your science notebook.

Online Lab - Lab 23: Identification of Cations in Solution

Purpose

The purpose of this online lab is to identify the ions in an unknown solution through the application of chemical tests.

Pre-Reading

Print and read the section of the workbook for the "Identification of Cations in Solution" online lab.

Procedure

- ✓ Do the lab entitled "Identification of Cations in Solution" and answer the questions as you work through the online lab.

Lab Notebook

- ☞ Add the completed workbook pages that were printed to the lab notebook.

Events in Science

Current Events

- 🕒 Find a current events article relating to the field of chemistry and complete the article summary sheet found on pg. 245 of the Appendix. Once you are done, add the sheet to the events section of your science notebook.

Historical Figures

- 🕒 Continue to research the life and work of Robert Boyle.

Hands-on Activity

Optional Hands-on

- ✂ Make a supersaturated solution and then let it sit to allow crystals to form. You will need a glass jar, pipe cleaner, string, pencil, water, and Borax. Directions can be found under #2 at the following post: https://elementalscience.com/blogs/science-activities/3-science-activities-you-can-do-with-borax.

Week 2 Supply List

Weekly Experiment	
Supplies from CK01B Chemistry Kit	❒ Goggles, Calcium nitrate, Centrifuge tube 15 mL, Pipettes, Reaction plate 24-well, Oxalic acid, Phenolphthalein, Sodium hydroxide
Additional Supplies From Home	❒ Gloves, Desk lamp or other strong light source, Paper or cloth (black),Water (distilled)
Hands-on Activity	
Supplies Needed	❒ Glass jar, Pipe cleaner, String, Pencil, Water, Borax

Week 2	Unit 3 (Honors Course)				5-Day
Weekly Topic					
➔ This week will begin a look at solutions.					
	Day 1	Day 2	Day 3	Day 4	Day 5
Textbook and Experiment	❐ Read *CK-12 Chemistry* Section 16.1.	❐ Read *CK-12 Chemistry* Section 16.2.	❐ Read the background and procedure sections for the week's lab.	❐ Do the "Determine a Solubility Product Constant" lab on pg. 112 in *The Home Scientist Chemistry Laboratory Manual*.	❐ Do the optional Hands-on Assignment - Crystals.
Writing	❐ Add the vocabulary to the glossary section of your science notebook.	❐ Answer the assigned questions in the reading section of your science notebook.	❐ Take the Chapter 15 Test from *CK-12 Chemistry*.	❐ Record what you have done in the lab section of your science notebook.	❐ Complete the lab review questions for the week.
Events in Science	❐ Choose one of the Events in Science assignments to do and add your work to the events section of your science notebook.				
Other Notes					

Week 2	Unit 3 (Standard Course)			4-Day
Weekly Topic				
➔ This week will begin a look at solutions.				
	Day 1	Day 2	Day 3	Day 4
Textbook and Experiment	❒ Read *CK-12 Chemistry* Section 16.1.	❒ Read *CK-12 Chemistry* Section 16.2.	❒ Read the background and procedure sections for the week's lab.	❒ Do the "Determine a Solubility Product Constant" lab on pg. 112 in *The Home Scientist Chemistry Laboratory Manual*. **OR** ❒ Do the online lab "Identification of Cations in Solution."
Writing	❒ Add the vocabulary to the glossary section of your science notebook.	❒ Answer the assigned questions in the reading section of your science notebook.	❒ Take the Chapter 15 Test from *CK-12 Chemistry*.	❒ Record what you have done in the lab section of your science notebook.
Other Notes				

Week 2	Unit 3 (Survey Course)	2-Day
	Weekly Topic	
➔ This week will begin a look at solutions.		
	Day 1	Day 2
Textbook	❐ Read *CK-12 Chemistry* Section 16.1.	❐ Read *CK-12 Chemistry* Section 16.2.
Writing	❐ Add the vocabulary to the glossary section of your science notebook. ❐ Take the Chapter 15 Test from *CK-12 Chemistry.*	❐ Answer the assigned questions in the reading section of your science notebook.
Events in Science	❐ Choose one of the Events in Science assignments to do and add your work to the events section of your science notebook.	
	Other Notes	

Week 3 Notes - Solutions, part 2

Textbook Assignments

Reading

🕮 *CK-12 Chemistry* Section 16.3, 16.4

Written

After you finish reading, answer questions #3-8 in section 16.3 and #1-6 in section 16.4. File your work in the reading section of your science notebook. Then, define the following terms in the glossary section of your science notebook:

- ☐ Boiling Point Elevation
- ☐ Colligative Property
- ☐ Freezing Point Depression
- ☐ Ionic Equation
- ☐ Spectator Ion
- ☐ Net Ionic Equation

Experiment - Determine Heat of Solution

Purpose

The purpose of this lab is to explain how to determine the heat of solution in the laboratory.

Pre-Reading

Read the background and procedure sections for the "Determine Heat of Solution" lab on pg. 132 in *The Home Scientist Chemistry Laboratory Manual.*

Procedure

✓ Do the lab entitled "Determine Heat of Solution" on pg. 132 in *The Home Scientist Chemistry Laboratory Manual.*

Lab Notebook

☞ Write down on a sheet of paper or type out your notes as you do the experiment. After you are done, print out your lab notes and add them to the lab section of your science notebook.

Lab Questions

Complete the multiple choice section of the "Determine Heat of Solution" lab on pg. 134 in *The Home Scientist Chemistry Laboratory Manual.* Record the answers in the lab section of your science notebook.

Online Lab - Lab 17: Heat of Fusion of Water

Purpose

The purpose of this online lab is to measure the heat of fusion of water using a calorimeter.

Pre-Reading

Print and read the section of the workbook for the "Heat of Fusion of Water" online lab.

Procedure

✓ Do the lab entitled "Heat of Fusion of Water" and answer the questions as you work through the online lab.

Lab Notebook

☞ Add the completed workbook pages that were printed to the lab notebook.

Events in Science

Current Events

🕒 Find a current events article relating to the field of chemistry and complete the article summary sheet found on pg. 245 of the Appendix. Once you are done, add the sheet to the events section of your science notebook.

Historical Figures

🕒 Continue to research the life and work of Robert Boyle.

Hands-on Activity

Optional Hands-on

✂ Test how the addition of salt affects the freezing point of water. You will need three cups, water, food coloring, salt, and an instant-read thermometer. Directions for this project can be found here: https://elementalscience.com/blogs/science-activities/83744963-which-one-freezes-first.

Week 3 Supply List

Weekly Experiment	
Supplies from CK01B Chemistry Kit	❒ Goggles, Beaker 100 mL, Cylinder-graduated 10 mL, Thermometer
Additional Supplies From Home	❒ Gloves, Balance (optional), Foam cup (with lid), Soda bottle 2-liter (empty), Sodium chloride (table salt)
Hands-on Activity	
Supplies Needed	❒ 3 Cups, Water, Food coloring, Salt, Instant-read thermometer

Week 3	Unit 3 (Honors Course)				5-Day
Weekly Topic					
➔ This week will wrap up a look at solutions.					
	Day 1	Day 2	Day 3	Day 4	Day 5
Textbook and Experiment	❒ Read *CK-12 Chemistry* Section 16.3.	❒ Read *CK-12 Chemistry* Section 16.4.	❒ Read the background and procedure sections for the week's lab.	❒ Do the "Determine Heat of Solution" lab on pg. 132 in *The Home Scientist Chemistry Laboratory Manual.*	❒ Do the optional Hands-on Assignment - Freezing Point.
Writing	❒ Add the vocabulary to the glossary section of your science notebook.	❒ Answer the assigned questions in the reading section of your science notebook.		❒ Record what you have done in the lab section of your science notebook.	❒ Complete the lab review questions for the week.
Events in Science	❒ Choose one of the Events in Science assignments to do and add your work to the events section of your science notebook.				
Other Notes					

Week 3	Unit 3 (Standard Course)			4-Day
Weekly Topic				
➔ This week will wrap up a look at solutions.				
	Day 1	Day 2	Day 3	Day 4
Textbook and Experiment	❒ Read *CK-12 Chemistry* Section 16.3.	❒ Read *CK-12 Chemistry* Section 16.4.	❒ Read the background and procedure sections for the week's lab.	❒ Do the "Determine Heat of Solution" lab on pg. 132 in *The Home Scientist Chemistry Laboratory Manual.* **OR** ❒ Do the online lab "Heat of Fusion of Water."
Writing	❒ Add the vocabulary to the glossary section of your science notebook.	❒ Answer the assigned questions in the reading section of your science notebook.		❒ Record what you have done in the lab section of your science notebook.
Other Notes				

Week 3	Unit 3 (Survey Course)	2-Day
Weekly Topic		
➔ This week will wrap up a look at solutions.		
	Day 1	Day 2
Textbook	❒ Read *CK-12 Chemistry* Section 16.3.	❒ Read *CK-12 Chemistry* Section 16.4.
Writing	❒ Add the vocabulary to the glossary section of your science notebook.	❒ Answer the assigned questions in the reading section of your science notebook.
Events in Science	❒ Choose one of the Events in Science assignments to do and add your work to the events section of your science notebook.	
Other Notes		

Week 4 Notes - Thermochemistry, part 1

Textbook Assignments

Reading

🕮 *CK-12 Chemistry* Sections 17.1, 17.2

Written

After you finish reading, answer questions #1-7 in section 17.1 and questions #4-7 in section 17.2. File your work in the reading section of your science notebook. Then, define the following terms in the glossary section of your science notebook:

- ☐ Heat Capacity
- ☐ Specific Heat
- ☐ Thermochemistry
- ☐ Chemical Potential Energy
- ☐ Enthalpy
- ☐ Heat of Reaction

Experiment - Measure Electrode Potentials

Purpose

The purpose of this lab is to explain how to measure electrode potentials.

Pre-Reading

Read the background and procedure sections for the "Measure Electrode Potentials" lab on pg. 153 in *The Home Scientist Chemistry Laboratory Manual.*

Procedure

✓ Do the lab entitled "Measure Electrode Potentials" on pg. 153 in *The Home Scientist Chemistry Laboratory Manual.*

Lab Notebook

☞ Write down on a sheet of paper or type out your notes as you do the experiment. After you are done, print out your lab notes and add them to the lab section of your science notebook.

Lab Questions

Complete the multiple choice section of the "Measure Electrode Potentials" lab on pg. 156 in *The Home Scientist Chemistry Laboratory Manual.* Record the answers in the lab section of your science notebook.

Online Lab - Lab 19: Heat of Combustion

Purpose

The purpose of this online lab is to measure the heat of combustion of sugar.

Pre-Reading

Print and read the section of the workbook for the "Heat of Combustion" online lab.

Procedure

✓ Do the lab entitled "Heat of Combustion" and answer the questions as you work through the online lab.

Lab Notebook

☞ Add the completed workbook pages that were printed to the lab notebook.

Events in Science

Current Events

🕒 Find a current events article relating to the field of water chemistry and complete the article summary sheet found on pg. 245 of the Appendix. Once you are done, add the sheet to the events section of your science notebook.

Historical Figures

🕒 Continue to research the life and work of Robert Boyle.

Hands-on Activity

Optional Hands-on

✂ Test how heat affects the formation of a mixture. You will need water, food coloring, and three clear cups. To the first cup, add a cup of ice cold water. To the second cup, add a cup of room temperature water. To the third cup, add a cup of hot water. Then, add five drops of food coloring and time how long it takes for the food coloring to fully mix into the water. (*You should see that the higher the temperature, the quicker the food coloring mixes with the water. This is because the water molecules have more energy, which means they are moving around faster, allowing the mixture to form more rapidly.*)

Week 4 Supply List

Weekly Experiment	
Supplies from CK01B Chemistry Kit	❒ Goggles, Alligator clip leads, Copper wire, Iron nail, Magnesium ribbon
Additional Supplies From Home	❒ Gloves, Aluminum foil, Digital multimeter (DMM), Knife, Lemon
Hands-on Activity	
Supplies Needed	❒ Water, Food coloring, 3 Clear cups

Week 4	Unit 3 (Honors Course)				5-Day
Weekly Topic					
➔ This week will begin a look at thermochemistry.					
	Day 1	Day 2	Day 3	Day 4	Day 5
Textbook and Experiment	❒ Read *CK-12 Chemistry* Section 17.1.	❒ Read *CK-12 Chemistry* Section 17.2.	❒ Read the background and procedure sections for the week's lab.	❒ Do the "Measure Electrode Potentials" lab on pg. 153 in *The Home Scientist Chemistry Laboratory Manual.*	❒ Do the optional Hands-on Assignment - Heat Effects.
Writing	❒ Add the vocabulary to the glossary section of your science notebook.	❒ Answer the assigned questions in the reading section of your science notebook.	❒ Take the Chapter 16 Test from *CK-12 Chemistry.*	❒ Record what you have done in the lab section of your science notebook.	❒ Complete the lab review questions for the week.
Events in Science	❒ Choose one of the Events in Science assignments to do and add your work to the events section of your science notebook.				
Other Notes					

Week 4	Unit 3 (Standard Course)			4-Day
Weekly Topic				
➔ This week will begin a look at thermochemistry.				
	Day 1	Day 2	Day 3	Day 4
Textbook and Experiment	❒ Read *CK-12 Chemistry* Section 17.1.	❒ Read *CK-12 Chemistry* Sections 17.2.	❒ Read the background and procedure sections for the week's lab.	❒ Do the "Measure Electrode Potentials" lab on pg. 153 in *The Home Scientist Chemistry Laboratory Manual.* **OR** ❒ Do the online lab "Heat of Combustion."
Writing	❒ Add the vocabulary to the glossary section of your science notebook.	❒ Answer the assigned questions in the reading section of your science notebook.	❒ Take the Chapter 16 Test from *CK-12 Chemistry.*	❒ Record what you have done in the lab section of your science notebook.
Other Notes				

Week 4	Unit 3 (Survey Course)	2-Day
	Weekly Topic	
➔ This week will begin a look at thermochemistry.		
	Day 1	Day 2
Textbook	❒ Read *CK-12 Chemistry* Section 17.1.	❒ Read *CK-12 Chemistry* Sections 17.2.
Writing	❒ Add the vocabulary to the glossary section of your science notebook. ❒ Take the Chapter 16 Test from *CK-12 Chemistry.*	❒ Answer the assigned questions in the reading section of your science notebook.
Events in Science	❒ Choose one of the Events in Science assignments to do and add your work to the events section of your science notebook.	
	Other Notes	

Week 5 Notes - Thermochemistry, part 2

Textbook Assignments

Reading

📖 *CK-12 Chemistry* Section 17.3, 17.4

Written

After you finish reading, answer questions #1-5 in section 17.3 and #3-6 in section 17.4 and file your work in the reading section of your science notebook. Then, define the following terms in the glossary section of your science notebook:

- ☐ Molar Heat of Condensation
- ☐ Molar Heat of Fusion
- ☐ Molar Heat of Vaporization
- ☐ Molar Heat of a Solution
- ☐ Hess's Law of Heat Summation
- ☐ Standard Heat of Formation

Experiment - Determine Heat of Fusion of Ice

Purpose

The purpose of this lab is to determine the heat of fusion of ice.

Pre-Reading

Read the background and procedure sections for the "Determine Heat of Fusion of Ice" lab on pg. 135 in *The Home Scientist Chemistry Laboratory Manual.*

Procedure

✓ Do the lab entitled "Determine Heat of Fusion of Ice" on pg. 135 in *The Home Scientist Chemistry Laboratory Manual.*

Lab Notebook

☞ Write down on a sheet of paper or type out your notes as you do the experiment. After you are done, print out your lab notes and add them to the lab section of your science notebook.

Lab Questions

Complete the multiple choice section of the "Determine Heat of Fusion of Ice" lab on pg. 136 in *The Home Scientist Chemistry Laboratory Manual.* Record the answers in the lab section of your science notebook.

Online Lab - Lab 18: Heats of Reaction

Purpose

The purpose of this online lab is to measure the heats of reaction for three related exothermic reactions and to verify Hess's law.

Pre-Reading

Print and read the section of the workbook for the "Heats of Reaction" online lab.

Procedure

✓ Do the lab entitled "Heats of Reaction" and answer the questions as you work through the online lab.

Lab Notebook

☞ Add the completed workbook pages that were printed to the lab notebook.

Events in Science

Current Events

🕒 Find a current events article relating to the field of water chemistry and complete the article summary sheet found on pg. 245 of the Appendix. Once you are done, add the sheet to the events section of your science notebook.

Historical Figures

🕒 Begin to work on your paper on the life and work of Robert Boyle. This week, aim to complete your outline. See pg. 14 for more directions. You will have three weeks to complete this paper.

Hands-on Activity

Optional Hands-on

✂ Measure the change in heat of a reaction. You will need epsom salts, water, a cup, and an instant-read thermometer. Add a cup of water to the cup and measure the temperature. With the thermometer in the water, add a tablespoon of epsom salts and record the temperature. Observe the solution for the next twenty minutes, recording the temperature every minute. (*You should see that the temperature of the solution immediately drops when you add the epsom salts, as this is an endothermic reaction. Over time, you should see the temperature approach room temperature again.*)

Week 5 Supply List

Weekly Experiment	
Supplies from CK01B Chemistry Kit	❒ Goggles, Beakers - 50 and 250 mL, Cylinder - graduated 10 mL, Thermometer
Additional Supplies From Home	❒ Gloves, Balance (optional), Foam cups (with lid), Ice
Hands-on Activity	
Supplies Needed	❒ Epsom salts, Water, Cup, Instant-read thermometer

Week 5	Unit 3 (Honors Course)				5-Day
Weekly Topic					
➔ This week will wrap up a look at thermochemistry.					
	Day 1	Day 2	Day 3	Day 4	Day 5
Textbook and Experiment	❒ Read *CK-12 Chemistry* Section 17.3.	❒ Read *CK-12 Chemistry* Section 17.4.	❒ Read the background and procedure sections for the week's lab.	❒ Do the "Determine Heat of Fusion of Ice" lab on pg. 135 in *The Home Scientist Chemistry Laboratory Manual.*	❒ Do the optional Hands-on Assignment - Phet Reaction Simulation.
Writing	❒ Add the vocabulary to the glossary section of your science notebook.	❒ Answer the assigned questions in the reading section of your science notebook.		❒ Record what you have done in the lab section of your science notebook.	❒ Complete the lab review questions for the week.
Events in Science	❒ Choose one of the Events in Science assignments to do and add your work to the events section of your science notebook.				
Other Notes					

Week 5	Unit 3 (Standard Course)			4-Day
Weekly Topic				
➔ This week will wrap up a look at thermochemistry.				
	Day 1	Day 2	Day 3	Day 4
Textbook and Experiment	❒ Read *CK-12 Chemistry* Section 17.3.	❒ Read *CK-12 Chemistry* Section 17.4.	❒ Read the background and procedure sections for the week's lab.	❒ Do the "Determine Heat of Fusion of Ice" lab on pg. 135 in *The Home Scientist Chemistry Laboratory Manual.* **OR** ❒ Do the online lab "Heats of Reaction."
Writing	❒ Add the vocabulary to the glossary section of your science notebook.	❒ Answer the assigned questions in the reading section of your science notebook.		❒ Record what you have done in the lab section of your science notebook.
Other Notes				

Week 5	Unit 3 (Survey Course)	2-Day
Weekly Topic		
➔ This week will wrap up a look at thermochemistry.		
	Day 1	Day 2
Textbook	❒ Read *CK-12 Chemistry* Section 17.3.	❒ Read *CK-12 Chemistry* Section 17.4.
Writing	❒ Add the vocabulary to the glossary section of your science notebook.	❒ Answer the assigned questions in the reading section of your science notebook.
Events in Science	❒ Choose one of the Events in Science assignments to do and add your work to the events section of your science notebook.	
Other Notes		

Week 6 Notes - Kinetics

Textbook Assignments

Reading

🕮 *CK-12 Chemistry* Sections 18.1, 18.2, 18.3

Written

After you finish reading, answer questions #5-9 in section 18.1, questions #6-7 in 18.2, and #5-7 in 18.3. File your work in the reading section of your science notebook. Then, define the following terms in the glossary section of your science notebook:

- ☐ Activated Complex
- ☐ Catalyst
- ☐ Collision Theory
- ☐ Molecularity
- ☐ First-Order Reaction
- ☐ Specific Rate Constant

Experiment - Determine the Specific Heat of a Metal

Purpose

The purpose of this lab is to determine the specific heat of a metal and record the results.

Pre-Reading

Read the background and procedure sections for the "Determine the Specific Heat of a Metal" lab on pg. 137 in *The Home Scientist Chemistry Laboratory Manual.*

Procedure

✓ Do the lab entitled "Determine the Specific Heat of a Metal" on pg. 137 in *The Home Scientist Chemistry Laboratory Manual.*

Lab Notebook

☞ Write down on a sheet of paper or type out your notes as you do the experiment. After you are done, print out your lab notes and add them to the lab section of your science notebook.

Lab Questions

Complete the multiple choice section of the "Determine the Specific Heat of a Metal" lab on pg. 140 in *The Home Scientist Chemistry Laboratory Manual.* Record the answers in the lab section of your science notebook.

Online Lab - Lab 16: The Specific Heat of a Metal

Purpose

The purpose of this online lab is to determine the specific heat of metals using a calorimeter.

Pre-Reading

Print and read the section of the workbook for the "The Specific Heat of a Metal" online lab.

Procedure

✓ Do the lab entitled "The Specific Heat of a Metal" and answer the questions as you work through the online lab.

Lab Notebook

☞ Add the completed workbook pages that were printed to the lab notebook.

Events in Science

Current Events

◷ Find a current events article relating to the field of water chemistry and complete the article summary sheet found on pg. 245 of the Appendix. Once you are done, add the sheet to the events section of your science notebook.

Historical Figures

◷ Continue work on your paper on the life and work of Robert Boyle. This week, aim to complete your rough draft. See pg. 14 for more directions.

Hands-on Activity

Optional Hands-on

✂ Use a catalyst to speed up a reaction. You will need hydrogen peroxide, dish soap, yeast, water, a bottle, and a cup. In the bottle, mix about a quarter of a cup of hydrogen peroxide with two teaspoons of dish soap. In the cup, mix a teaspoon of yeast with a two tablespoons of room temperature water. Let the mixtures sit for about a minute and observe what happens. Then, add the cup mixture to the mixture in the bottle and observe what happens. (*Hydrogen peroxide slowly decomposes into water and oxygen gas as soon as it is exposed to light. The yeast in this reaction acts as a catalyst to speed up this reaction, forming a lot of oxygen gas in a small amount of time. This gas is captured by the dish soap, causing the mixture to come up and out of the bottle.*)

Week 6 Supply List

Weekly Experiment	
Supplies from CK01B Chemistry Kit	❒ Goggles, Beakers - 100 mL and 250 mL, Thermometer
Additional Supplies From Home	❒ Gloves, Balance (optional), Foam cup (with lid), Microwave oven, Paper towels, US cent coins
Hands-on Activity	
Supplies Needed	❒ Hydrogen peroxide, Dish soap, Yeast, Water, Bottle, Cup

Week 6	Unit 3 (Honors Course)				5-Day
Weekly Topic					
➔ This week will look at kinetics.					
	Day 1	Day 2	Day 3	Day 4	Day 5
Textbook and Experiment	❒ Read *CK-12 Chemistry* Sections 18.1 and 18.2.	❒ Read *CK-12 Chemistry* Section 18.3.	❒ Read the background and procedure sections for the week's lab.	❒ Do the "Determine the Specific Heat of a Metal" lab on pg. 137 in *The Home Scientist Chemistry Laboratory Manual.*	❒ Do the optional Hands-on Assignment - Catalyst.
Writing	❒ Add the vocabulary to the glossary section of your science notebook.	❒ Answer the assigned questions in the reading section of your science notebook.	❒ Take the Chapter 17 Test from *CK-12 Chemistry.*	❒ Record what you have done in the lab section of your science notebook.	❒ Complete the lab review questions for the week.
Events in Science	❒ Choose one of the Events in Science assignments to do and add your work to the events section of your science notebook.				
Other Notes					

Week 6 Unit 3 (Standard Course) 4-Day

Weekly Topic

➔ This week will look at kinetics.

	Day 1	Day 2	Day 3	Day 4
Textbook and Experiment	❒ Read *CK-12 Chemistry* Sections 18.1 and 18.2.	❒ Read *CK-12 Chemistry* Section 18.3.	❒ Read the background and procedure sections for the week's lab.	❒ Do the "Determine the Specific Heat of a Metal" lab on pg. 137 in *The Home Scientist Chemistry Laboratory Manual.* **OR** ❒ Do the online lab "The Specific Heat of a Metal."
Writing	❒ Add the vocabulary to the glossary section of your science notebook.	❒ Answer the assigned questions in the reading section of your science notebook.	❒ Take the Chapter 17 Test from *CK-12 Chemistry.*	❒ Record what you have done in the lab section of your science notebook.

Other Notes

Week 6	Unit 3 (Survey Course)	2-Day
Weekly Topic		
➔ This week will look at kinetics.		
	Day 1	Day 2
Textbook	❒ Read *CK-12 Chemistry* Sections 18.1 and 18.2.	❒ Read *CK-12 Chemistry* Section 18.3.
Writing	❒ Add the vocabulary to the glossary section of your science notebook. ❒ Take the Chapter 17 Test from *CK-12 Chemistry.*	❒ Answer the assigned questions in the reading section of your science notebook.
Events in Science	❒ Choose one of the Events in Science assignments to do and add your work to the events section of your science notebook.	
Other Notes		

Week 7 Notes - Equilibrium

Textbook Assignments

Reading

📖 *CK-12 Chemistry* Sections 19.1, 19.2, 19.3

Written

After you finish reading, answer questions #4-7 in section 19.1, #2-6 in section 19.2 and #3-7 in section 19.3. File your work in the reading section of your science notebook. Then, define the following terms in the glossary section of your science notebook:

- ☐ Chemical Equilibrium
- ☐ Equilibrium Constant
- ☐ Reversible Reaction
- ☐ Le Chatelier's Principle
- ☐ Common Ion Effect
- ☐ Solubility Product Constant

Experiment - Determine the Enthalpy Change of a Reaction

Purpose

The purpose of this lab is to to determine the entalpy change of a reaction.

Pre-Reading

Read the background and procedure sections for the "Determine the Enthalpy Change of a Reaction" lab on pg. 141 in *The Home Scientist Chemistry Laboratory Manual.*

Procedure

✓ Do the lab entitled "Determine the Enthalpy Change of a Reaction" on pg. 141 in *The Home Scientist Chemistry Laboratory Manual.*

Lab Notebook

☞ Write down on a sheet of paper or type out your notes as you do the experiment. After you are done, print out your lab notes and add them to the lab section of your science notebook.

Lab Questions

Complete the multiple choice section of the "Determine the Enthalpy Change of a Reaction" lab on pg. 143 in *The Home Scientist Chemistry Laboratory Manual.* Record the answers in the lab section of your science notebook.

Online Lab - Lab 20: Enthalpy and Entropy

Purpose

The purpose of this online lab is to observe and measure energy changes during the formation of a solution and to describe and explain those changes in terms of entropy and enthalpy.

Pre-Reading

Print and read the section of the workbook for the "Enthalpy and Entropy" online lab.

Procedure

✓ Do the lab entitled "Enthalpy and Entropy" and answer the questions as you work through the online lab.

Lab Notebook

☞ Add the completed workbook pages that were printed to the lab notebook.

Events in Science

Current Events

🕒 Find a current events article relating to the field of water chemistry and complete the article summary sheet found on pg. 245 of the Appendix. Once you are done, add the sheet to the events section of your science notebook.

Historical Figures

🕒 Continue work on your paper on the life and work of Robert Boyle. This week, aim to complete your final draft. See pg. 14 for more directions.

Hands-on Activity

Optional Hands-on

✂ Watch another equilibrium reaction that is affected by temperature: Equilibrium in Nitrogen Dioxide Gas - https://www.youtube.com/watch?v=zVZXq64HSV4

Week 7 Supply List

Weekly Experiment	
Supplies from CK01B Chemistry Kit	❒ Goggles, Graduated cylinder 10 mL, Hydrochloric acid 6 M, Sodium hydroxide 6 M, Thermometer
Additional Supplies From Home	❒ Gloves, Foam cup (with lid)
Hands-on Activity	
Supplies Needed	❒ None

Week 7	Unit 3 (Honors Course)				5-Day
Weekly Topic					
➔ This week will look at equilibrium.					
	Day 1	Day 2	Day 3	Day 4	Day 5
Textbook and Experiment	❐ Read *CK-12 Chemistry* Sections 19.1 and 19.2.	❐ Read *CK-12 Chemistry* Section 19.3.	❐ Read the background and procedure sections for the week's lab.	❐ Do the "Determine the Enthalpy Change of a Reaction" lab on pg. 141 in *The Home Scientist Chemistry Laboratory Manual*.	❐ Do the optional Hands-on Assignment - Equilibrium Video
Writing	❐ Add the vocabulary to the glossary section of your science notebook.	❐ Answer the assigned questions in the reading section of your science notebook.	❐ Take the Chapter 18 Test from *CK-12 Chemistry*.	❐ Record what you have done in the lab section of your science notebook.	❐ Complete the lab review questions for the week.
Events in Science	❐ Choose one of the Events in Science assignments to do and add your work to the events section of your science notebook.				
Other Notes					

Week 7	Unit 3 (Standard Course)			4-Day
Weekly Topic				
➔ This week will look at equilibrium.				
	Day 1	Day 2	Day 3	Day 4
Textbook and Experiment	❒ Read *CK-12 Chemistry* Sections 19.1 and 19.2.	❒ Read *CK-12 Chemistry* Section 19.3.	❒ Read the background and procedure sections for the week's lab.	❒ Do the "Determine the Enthalpy Change of a Reaction" lab on pg. 141 in *The Home Scientist Chemistry Laboratory Manual.* **OR** ❒ Do the online lab "Enthalpy and Entropy."
Writing	❒ Add the vocabulary to the glossary section of your science notebook.	❒ Answer the assigned questions in the reading section of your science notebook.	❒ Take the Chapter 18 Test from *CK-12 Chemistry.*	❒ Record what you have done in the lab section of your science notebook.
Other Notes				

Week 7	Unit 3 (Survey Course)	2-Day
	Weekly Topic	
➔ This week will look at equilibrium.		
	Day 1	Day 2
Textbook	❒ Read *CK-12 Chemistry* Sections 19.1 and 19.2.	❒ Read *CK-12 Chemistry* Section 19.3.
Writing	❒ Add the vocabulary to the glossary section of your science notebook. ❒ Take the Chapter 18 Test from *CK-12 Chemistry.*	❒ Answer the assigned questions in the reading section of your science notebook.
Events in Science	❒ Choose one of the Events in Science assignments to do and add your work to the events section of your science notebook.	
	Other Notes	

Week 8 Notes - Entropy and Free Energy

Textbook Assignments

Reading

📖 *CK-12 Chemistry* Sections 20.1, 20.2, 20.3

Written

After you finish reading, answer questions #1-7 in section 20.1, #8-9 in section 20.2, and #1-7 in section 20.3 and file your work in the reading section of your science notebook. Then, define the following terms in the glossary section of your science notebook:

- ☐ Entropy
- ☐ Free Energy
- ☐ Non-spontaneous Reaction
- ☐ Spontaneous Reaction

Experiment

☞ There is no experiment scheduled for this week. Instead, take some time to learn more about entropy by watching this TedEd video: https://www.youtube.com/watch?v=YM-uykVfq_E.

Online Lab

☞ There is no online lab scheduled for this week.

Events in Science

Current Events

🕒 There is no assignment for this week.

Historical Figures

🕒 There is no assignment for this week.

Hands-on Activity

Optional Hands-on

✂ Create a bit of entropy with a balloon and scissors. Blow up a balloon and tie off the end. Next, use the scissors to cut a hole in the ballon and observe what happens. (*You should see the air quickly escape out of the hole you cut in the balloon thanks to entropy.*)

Week 8 Supply List

Weekly Experiment	
Supplies from CK01B Chemistry Kit	❒ None
Additional Supplies From Home	❒ None
Hands-on Activity	
Supplies Needed	❒ Balloon, Scissors

Week 8	Unit 3 (Honors Course)				5-Day
Weekly Topic					
➔ This week will look at entropy and free energy.					
	Day 1	Day 2	Day 3	Day 4	Day 5
Textbook and Experiment	❒ Read *CK-12 Chemistry* Sections 20.1 and 20.2.	❒ Read *CK-12 Chemistry* Section 20.3.	❒ Watch the TedEd Entropy Video.	❒ Take the Chapter 19 Test from *CK-12 Chemistry*.	❒ Do the optional Hands-on Assignment - Entropy Balloon.
Writing	❒ Add the vocabulary to the glossary section of your science notebook.	❒ Answer the assigned questions in the reading section of your science notebook.			
Other Notes					

Week 8	Unit 3 (Standard Course)			4-Day
Weekly Topic				
➔ This week will look at entropy and free energy.				
	Day 1	Day 2	Day 3	Day 4
Textbook and Experiment	❒ Read *CK-12 Chemistry* Sections 20.1 and 20.2.	❒ Read *CK-12 Chemistry* Section 20.3.	❒ Watch the TedEd Entropy Video.	❒ Take the Chapter 19 Test from *CK-12 Chemistry*.
Writing	❒ Add the vocabulary to the glossary section of your science notebook.	❒ Answer the assigned questions in the reading section of your science notebook.		
Other Notes				

Week 8	Unit 3 (Survey Course)	2-Day
Weekly Topic		
➔ This week will look at entropy and free energy.		
	Day 1	Day 2
Textbook	❒ Read *CK-12 Chemistry* Sections 20.1 and 20.2.	❒ Read *CK-12 Chemistry* Section 20.3.
Writing	❒ Add the vocabulary to the glossary section of your science notebook. ❒ Take the Chapter 19 Test from *CK-12 Chemistry*.	❒ Answer the assigned questions in the reading section of your science notebook.
Other Notes		

Chemistry for High School

Unit 4 - Organic Chemistry and More

Week 1 Notes - Acids and Bases, Part 1

Textbook Assignments

Reading

📖 *CK-12 Chemistry* Section 21.1, 21.2, 21.3

Written

After you finish reading, answer questions #3-6 in section 21.1, #5-6 in section 21.2, and #1-5 in section 21.3. File your work in the reading section of your science notebook. Then, define the following terms in the glossary section of your science notebook:

- ☐ Amphoteric
- ☐ Arrhenius Acid
- ☐ Conjugate Acid
- ☐ Lewis Acid
- ☐ Lewis Base
- ☐ Monoprotic Acid
- ☐ Polyprotic Acid
- ☐ Self-ionization
- ☐ Acid Ionization Constant
- ☐ Base Ionization Constant

Experiment - Determine the Effect of Concentration on pH and the pH of Household Materials

Purpose

The purpose of this lab is to determine the effect of concentration on pH and to look at the pH range of indicators.

Pre-Reading

Read the background and procedure sections for the "Determine the Effect of Concentration on pH and the pH of Household Materials" lab on pg. 81 in *The Home Scientist Chemistry Laboratory Manual.*

Procedure

✓ Do the lab entitled "Determine the Effect of Concentration on pH and the pH of Household Materials" on pg. 81 in *The Home Scientist Chemistry Laboratory Manual.*

Lab Notebook

☞ Write down on a sheet of paper or type out your notes as you do the experiment. After you are done, print out your lab notes and add them to the lab section of your science notebook.

Lab Questions

Complete the multiple choice section of the "Determine the Effect of Concentration on pH and the pH of Household Materials" lab on pg. 87 in *The Home Scientist Chemistry Laboratory Manual.* Record the answers in the lab section of your science notebook.

Online Lab - Lab 25: Study of Acid-Base Titrations

Purpose

The purpose of this online lab is to observe the changes that occur during the titration of a strong acid and strong base.

Pre-Reading

- Print and read the section of the workbook for the "Study of Acid-Base Titrations" online lab.

Procedure

- ✓ Do the lab entitled "Study of Acid-Base Titrations" and answer the questions as you work through the online lab.

Lab Notebook

- Add the completed workbook pages that were printed to the lab notebook.

Events in Science

Current Events

- Find a current events article relating to the field of chemistry and complete the article summary sheet found on pg. 245 of the Appendix. Once you are done, add the sheet to the events section of your science notebook.

Historical Figures

- Begin to research the life and work of Marie Curie, who discovered radium and polonium. You will have five weeks to complete your research. After that, you will have three weeks to prepare a two to three page paper on this scientist and his contributions to the field of chemistry.

Hands-on Activity

Optional Hands-on

- Test some of the items in your home to see if they are acids or bases. You will need a head of red cabbage and a variety of items from your kitchen to test, such as lemon juice, baking soda, soda, or detergent. Directions for this activity can be found here: https://elementalscience.com/blogs/science-activities/kitchen-acid-test. (*Save some of the cabbage juice you make this week for next week's hands-on activity.*)

Week 1 Supply List

Weekly Experiment	
Supplies from CK01B Chemistry Kit	❐ Goggles, Beaker - 100 mL polypropylene, Graduated cylinder - 10 mL, Pipettes, Reaction plate (24-well), Stirring rod, pH test paper wide-range, Acetic acid 6M, Ammonia 6M, Hydrochloric acid 6M, Sodium hydroxide 6M, Test tubes - PP 15 mL, Test tube rack
Additional Supplies From Home	❐ Gloves, Household materials to test (see text), Scissors, Distilled water
Hands-on Activity	
Supplies Needed	❐ Head a red cabbage, Variety of items from your kitchen to test (such as lemon juice, baking soda, soda, or detergent)

Week 1	Unit 4 (Honors Course)				5-Day
	Weekly Topic				
➔ This week will begin a look at acids and bases.					
	Day 1	Day 2	Day 3	Day 4	Day 5
Textbook and Experiment	❒ Read *CK-12 Chemistry* Sections 21.1 and 21.2.	❒ Read *CK-12 Chemistry* Section 21.3.	❒ Read the background and procedure sections for the week's lab.	❒ Do the "Determine the Effect of Concentration on pH" lab on pg. 81 in *The Home Scientist Chemistry Laboratory Manual*.	❒ Do the optional Hands-on Assignment - Kitchen Acids and Bases.
Writing	❒ Add the vocabulary to the glossary section of your science notebook.	❒ Answer the assigned questions in the reading section of your science notebook.	❒ Take the Chapter 20 Test from *CK-12 Chemistry*.	❒ Record what you have done in the lab section of your science notebook.	❒ Complete the lab review questions for the week.
Events in Science	❒ Choose one of the Events in Science assignments to do and add your work to the events section of your sciencc notebook.				
	Other Notes				

Week 1	Unit 4 (Standard Course)			4-Day
Weekly Topic				
➔ This week will begin a look at acids and bases.				
	Day 1	Day 2	Day 3	Day 4
Textbook and Experiment	❐ Read *CK-12 Chemistry* Sections 21.1 and 21.2.	❐ Read *CK-12 Chemistry* Section 21.3.	❐ Read the background and procedure sections for the week's lab.	❐ Do the "Determine the Effect of Concentration on pH" lab on pg. 81 in *The Home Scientist Chemistry Laboratory Manual.* **OR** ❐ Do the online lab "Study of Acid-Base Titrations."
Writing	❐ Add the vocabulary to the glossary section of your science notebook.	❐ Answer the assigned questions in the reading section of your science notebook.	❐ Take the Chapter 20 Test from *CK-12 Chemistry.*	❐ Record what you have done in the lab section of your science notebook.
Other Notes				

Week 1	Unit 4 (Survey Course)	2-Day
Weekly Topic		
➔ This week will begin a look at acids and bases.		
	Day 1	Day 2
Textbook	❒ Read *CK-12 Chemistry* Sections 21.1 and 21.2.	❒ Read *CK-12 Chemistry* Section 21.3.
Writing	❒ Add the vocabulary to the glossary section of your science notebook. ❒ Take the Chapter 20 Test from *CK-12 Chemistry*.	❒ Answer the assigned questions in the reading section of your science notebook.
Events in Science	❒ Choose one of the Events in Science assignments to do and add your work to the events section of your science notebook.	
Other Notes		

Week 2 Notes - Acids and Bases, Part 2

Textbook Assignments

Reading

🕮 *CK-12 Chemistry* Sections 21.4, 21.5

Written

After you finish reading, answer questions #1-7 in section 21.4 and questions #1-7 in section 21.5. File your work in the reading section of your science notebook. Then, define the following terms in the glossary section of your science notebook:

- ☐ End Point
- ☐ Equivalence Point
- ☐ Neutralization Reaction
- ☐ Standard Solution
- ☐ Titration
- ☐ Titration Curve
- ☐ Buffer Capacity

Experiment - Determine the Molarity of Vinegar by Titration

Purpose

The purpose of this lab is to determine the molarity of vinegar by titration.

Pre-Reading

Read the background and procedure sections for the "Determine the Molarity of Vinegar by Titration" lab on pg. 88 in *The Home Scientist Chemistry Laboratory Manual.*

Procedure

✓ Do the lab entitled "Determine the Molarity of Vinegar by Titration" on pg. 88 in *The Home Scientist Chemistry Laboratory Manual.*

Lab Notebook

☞ Write down on a sheet of paper or type out your notes as you do the experiment. After you are done, print out your lab notes and add them to the lab section of your science notebook.

Lab Questions

Complete the multiple choice section of the "Determine the Molarity of Vinegar by Titration" lab on pg. 91 in *The Home Scientist Chemistry Laboratory Manual.* Record the answers in the lab section of your science notebook.

Online Lab - Lab 26: Acid Base Titrations

Purpose

The purpose of this online lab is to learn how to standardize a NaOH solution and to measure the molarity of an unknown acetic acid solution by titration with standardized NaOH.

Pre-Reading

Print and read the section of the workbook for the "Acid Base Titrations" online lab.

Procedure

✓ Do the lab entitled "Acid Base Titrations" and answer the questions as you work through the online lab.

Lab Notebook

☞ Add the completed workbook pages that were printed to the lab notebook.

Events in Science

Current Events

🕒 Find a current events article relating to the field of chemistry and complete the article summary sheet found on pg. 245 of the Appendix. Once you are done, add the sheet to the events section of your science notebook.

Historical Figures

🕒 Continue to research the life and work of Marie Curie.

Hands-on Activity

Optional Hands-on

✂ Neutralize an acid with a base. You will need white vinegar, ammonia, water, cabbage juice indicator, an eyedropper, and a cup. Pour half a cup of vinegar into the cup and add two tablespoons of cabbage juice indicator. (*The solution should turn pink.*) Use the eyedropper to add ammonia to the cup until you reach a neutral purple color. (*Be sure to record how many drops it takes to neutralize the solution.*)

Week 2 Supply List

Weekly Experiment	
Supplies from CK01B Chemistry Kit	❒ Goggles, Bromothymol blue, Centrifuge tube - 15 mL, Phenolphthalein, Reaction plate 24-well, Sodium bicarbonate tablet
Additional Supplies From Home	❒ Gloves, Desk lamp (or other strong light source), Distilled water, Paper, Vinegar-distilled white
Hands-on Activity	
Supplies Needed	❒ White vinegar, Ammonia, Water, Cabbage juice indicator, (*from week 1*) Eyedropper, Cup

Week 2	Unit 4 (Honors Course)				5-Day
Weekly Topic					
➔ This week will wrap up a look at acids and bases.					
	Day 1	Day 2	Day 3	Day 4	Day 5
Textbook and Experiment	❒ Read *CK-12 Chemistry* Section 21.4.	❒ Read *CK-12 Chemistry* Section 21.5.	❒ Read the background and procedure sections for the week's lab.	❒ Do the "Determine the Molarity of Vinegar by Titration" lab on pg. 88 in *The Home Scientist Chemistry Laboratory Manual*.	❒ Do the optional Hands-on Assignment - Acid Neutralization.
Writing	❒ Add the vocabulary to the glossary section of your science notebook.	❒ Answer the assigned questions in the reading section of your science notebook.		❒ Record what you have done in the lab section of your science notebook.	❒ Complete the lab review questions for the week.
Events in Science	❒ Choose one of the Events in Science assignments to do and add your work to the events section of your science notebook.				
Other Notes					

Week 2	Unit 4 (Standard Course)			4-Day
Weekly Topic				
➔ This week will wrap up a look at acids and bases.				
	Day 1	Day 2	Day 3	Day 4
Textbook and Experiment	❒ Read *CK-12 Chemistry* Section 21.4.	❒ Read *CK-12 Chemistry* Section 21.5.	❒ Read the background and procedure sections for the week's lab.	❒ Do the "Determine the Molarity of Vinegar by Titration" lab on pg. 88 in *The Home Scientist Chemistry Laboratory Manual.* **OR** ❒ Do the online lab "Acid Base Titrations."
Writing	❒ Add the vocabulary to the glossary section of your science notebook.	❒ Answer the assigned questions in the reading section of your science notebook.		❒ Record what you have done in the lab section of your science notebook.
Other Notes				

Week 2	Unit 4 (Survey Course)	2-Day
Weekly Topic		
➔ This week will wrap up a look at acids and bases.		
	Day 1	Day 2
Textbook	❒ Read *CK-12 Chemistry* Section 21.4.	❒ Read *CK-12 Chemistry* Section 21.5.
Writing	❒ Add the vocabulary to the glossary section of your science notebook.	❒ Answer the assigned questions in the reading section of your science notebook.
Events in Science	❒ Choose one of the Events in Science assignments to do and add your work to the events section of your science notebook.	
Other Notes		

Week 3 Notes - Oxidation-Reduction Reactions

Textbook Assignments

Reading

📖 *CK-12 Chemistry* Section 22.1, 22.2, 22.3

Written

After you finish reading, answer questions #5-7 in section 22.1, #4-6 in section 22.2 and #5-8 in section 22.3 and file your work in the reading section of your science notebook. Then, define the following terms in the glossary section of your science notebook:

- ☐ Reducing Agent
- ☐ Reduction
- ☐ Oxidation-Reduction reaction (redox)
- ☐ Oxidation Number
- ☐ Half-Reaction

Experiment - Observe Oxidation States of Manganese

Purpose

The purpose of this lab is to describe and balance a redox reaction, to perform a titration, and to use experimental data and stoichiometry to calculate molarity, percentages, and other results.

Pre-Reading

Read the background and procedure sections for the "Observe Oxidation States of Manganese" lab on pg. 76 in *The Home Scientist Chemistry Laboratory Manual.*

Procedure

✓ Do the lab entitled "Observe Oxidation States of Manganese" on pg. 76 in *The Home Scientist Chemistry Laboratory Manual.*

Lab Notebook

☞ Write down on a sheet of paper or type out your notes as you do the experiment. After you are done, print out your lab notes and add them to the lab section of your science notebook.

Lab Questions

Complete the multiple choice section of the "Observe Oxidation States of Manganese" lab on pg. 78 in *The Home Scientist Chemistry Laboratory Manual.* Record the answers in the lab section of your science notebook.

Online Lab - Lab 27: Ionization Constants of Weak Acids

Purpose

The purpose of this online lab is to measure ionization constants of weak acids such as bromocresol green (BCG).

Pre-Reading

Print and read the section of the workbook for the "Ionization Constants of Weak Acids" online lab.

Procedure

✓ Do the lab entitled "Ionization Constants of Weak Acids" and answer the questions as you work through the online lab.

Lab Notebook

☞ Add the completed workbook pages that were printed to the lab notebook.

Events in Science

Current Events

◷ Find a current events article relating to the field of chemistry and complete the article summary sheet found on pg. 245 of the Appendix. Once you are done, add the sheet to the events section of your science notebook.

Historical Figures

◷ Continue to research the life and work of Marie Curie.

Hands-on Activity

Optional Hands-on

✂ Clean a bit of silver with an oxidation-reduction reaction. You will need a piece of silver, aluminum foil, a heat-resistant container, hot water, baking soda, and salt. Directions for this activity can be found here: https://elementalscience.com/blogs/science-activities/silver-polish-summer-science-activity.

Week 3 Supply List

Weekly Experiment	
Supplies from CK01B Chemistry Kit	❒ Goggles, Graduated cylinder 10 mL, Pipettes, Reaction plate 24-well, Hydrochloric acid 6M, Potassium permanganate 0.1M, Sodium bisulfite 1.0M, Sodium hydroxide 6M
Additional Supplies From Home	❒ Gloves, Desk lamp or other strong light source, Sheet of white paper, Toothpicks, Distilled water
Hands-on Activity	
Supplies Needed	❒ Piece of silver, Aluminum foil, Heat-resistant container, Hot water, Baking soda, Salt

Week 3	Unit 4 (Honors Course)				5-Day
Weekly Topic					
➔ This week will look at oxidation-reduction reactions.					
	Day 1	Day 2	Day 3	Day 4	Day 5
Textbook and Experiment	❒ Read *CK-12 Chemistry* Sections 22.1 and 22.2.	❒ Read *CK-12 Chemistry* Section 22.3.	❒ Read the background and procedure sections for the week's lab.	❒ Do the "Observe Oxidation States of Manganese" lab on pg. 76 in *The Home Scientist Chemistry Laboratory Manual*.	❒ Do the optional Hands-on Assignment - Silver Cleaning.
Writing	❒ Add the vocabulary to the glossary section of your science notebook.	❒ Answer the assigned questions in the reading section of your science notebook.	❒ Take the Chapter 21 Test from *CK-12 Chemistry*.	❒ Record what you have done in the lab section of your science notebook.	❒ Complete the lab review questions for the week.
Events in Science	❒ Choose one of the Events in Science assignments to do and add your work to the events section of your science notebook.				
Other Notes					

Week 3	Unit 4 (Standard Course)			4-Day
Weekly Topic				
➔ This week will look at oxidation-reduction reactions.				
	Day 1	Day 2	Day 3	Day 4
Textbook and Experiment	❒ Read *CK-12 Chemistry* Sections 22.1 and 22.2.	❒ Read *CK-12 Chemistry* Section 22.3.	❒ Read the background and procedure sections for the week's lab.	❒ Do the "Observe Oxidation States of Manganese" lab on pg. 76 in *The Home Scientist Chemistry Laboratory Manual.* **OR** ❒ Do the online lab "Ionization Constants of Weak Acids."
Writing	❒ Add the vocabulary to the glossary section of your science notebook.	❒ Answer the assigned questions in the reading section of your science notebook.	❒ Take the Chapter 21 Test from *CK-12 Chemistry.*	❒ Record what you have done in the lab section of your science notebook.
Other Notes				

Week 3	Unit 4 (Survey Course)	2-Day
Weekly Topic		
➔ This week will look at oxidation-reduction reactions.		
	Day 1	Day 2
Textbook	❒ Read *CK-12 Chemistry* Sections 22.1 and 22.2.	❒ Read *CK-12 Chemistry* Section 22.3.
Writing	❒ Add the vocabulary to the glossary section of your science notebook. ❒ Take the Chapter 21 Test from *CK-12 Chemistry*.	❒ Answer the assigned questions in the reading section of your science notebook.
Events in Science	❒ Choose one of the Events in Science assignments to do and add your work to the events section of your science notebook.	
Other Notes		

Week 4 Notes - Electrochemistry

Textbook Assignments

Reading

📖 *CK-12 Chemistry* Sections 23.1, 23.2, 23.3

Written

After you finish reading, answer questions #4-7 in section 23.1, #5-7 in section 23.2, and #1-5 in section 23.3. File your work in the reading section of your science notebook. Then, define the following terms in the glossary section of your science notebook:

- ☐ Anode
- ☐ Electrochemical Cell
- ☐ Fuel Cell
- ☐ Half-cell
- ☐ Salt Bridge
- ☐ Voltaic Cell
- ☐ Cell Potential
- ☐ Reduction Potential
- ☐ Electrolytic Cell

Experiment - Photochemical Reaction of Iodine and Oxalate

Purpose

The purpose of this lab is to describe a neutralization reaction with a balanced reaction and demonstrate a neutralization reaction.

Pre-Reading

👓 Read the background and procedure sections for the "Photochemical Reaction of Iodine and Oxalate" lab on pg. 158 in *The Home Scientist Chemistry Laboratory Manual.*

Procedure

✓ Do the lab entitled "Photochemical Reaction of Iodine and Oxalate" on pg. 158 in *The Home Scientist Chemistry Laboratory Manual.*

Lab Notebook

☞ Write down on a sheet of paper or type out your notes as you do the experiment. After you are done, print out your lab notes and add them to the lab section of your science notebook.

Lab Questions

📌 Complete the multiple choice section of the "Photochemical Reaction of Iodine and Oxalate" lab on pg. 161 in *The Home Scientist Chemistry Laboratory Manual.* Record the answers in the lab section of your science notebook.

Online Lab - Lab 28: Analysis of Baking Soda

Purpose

The purpose of this online lab is to determine the mass of sodium hydrogen carbonate in a sample of baking soda using stoichiometry.

Pre-Reading

👓 Print and read the section of the workbook for the "Analysis of Baking Soda" online lab.

Procedure

✓ Do the lab entitled "Analysis of Baking Soda" and answer the questions as you work through the online lab.

Lab Notebook

☞ Add the completed workbook pages that were printed to the lab notebook.

Events in Science

Current Events

🕒 Find a current events article relating to the field of chemistry and complete the article summary sheet found on pg. 245 of the Appendix. Once you are done, add the sheet to the events section of your science notebook.

Historical Figures

🕒 Continue to research the life and work of Marie Curie.

Hands-on Activity

Optional Hands-on

✂ Use a bit of electrochemistry to make a lemon battery. You will need a LED bulb, four lemons (fresh and juicy), four clean pennies, four galvanized nails, five alligator clips, and wire. Directions for this activity can be found here: http://www.buzzle.com/articles/lemon-battery-experiment.html.

Week 4 Supply List

Weekly Experiment	
Supplies from CK01B Chemistry Kit	❒ Goggles, Ammonia 6 M, Graduated cylinder 10 mL, Iodine/iodide solution 0.1 M, Oxalic acid 0.5 M, Pipettes, Reaction plate 24-well, Sharpie marking pen, Test tubes-plastic, Test tube rack
Additional Supplies From Home	❒ Gloves, Aluminum foil, Desk lamp or other incandescent light, Fluorescent light source, Foam cups, Paper (white copy or similar), Water-distilled, Watch or clock
Hands-on Activity	
Supplies Needed	❒ LED bulb, 4 Lemons (fresh and juicy), 4 Clean pennies, 4 Galvanized nails, 5 Alligator clips, Wire

Week 4	Unit 4 (Honors Course)				5-Day
Weekly Topic					
➔ This week will look at electrochemistry.					
	Day 1	Day 2	Day 3	Day 4	Day 5
Textbook and Experiment	❒ Read *CK-12 Chemistry* Sections 23.1 and 23.2.	❒ Read *CK-12 Chemistry* Section 23.3.	❒ Read the background and procedure sections for the week's lab.	❒ Do the "Photochemical Reaction of Iodine and Oxalate" lab on pg. 158 in *The Home Scientist Chemistry Laboratory Manual.*	❒ Do the optional Hands-on Assignment - Lemon Battery.
Writing	❒ Add the vocabulary to the glossary section of your science notebook.	❒ Answer the assigned questions in the reading section of your science notebook.	❒ Take the Chapter 22 Test from *CK-12 Chemistry.*	❒ Record what you have done in the lab section of your science notebook.	❒ Complete the lab review questions for the week.
Events in Science	❒ Choose one of the Events in Science assignments to do and add your work to the events section of your science notebook.				
Other Notes					

Week 4	Unit 4 (Standard Course)			4-Day
Weekly Topic				
➔ This week will look at electrochemistry.				
	Day 1	Day 2	Day 3	Day 4
Textbook and Experiment	❒ Read *CK-12 Chemistry* Sections 23.1 and 23.2.	❒ Read *CK-12 Chemistry* Section 23.3.	❒ Read the background and procedure sections for the week's lab.	❒ Do the "Photochemical Reaction of Iodine and Oxalate" lab on pg. 158 in *The Home Scientist Chemistry Laboratory Manual.* **OR** ❒ Do the online lab "Analysis of Baking Soda."
Writing	❒ Add the vocabulary to the glossary section of your science notebook.	❒ Answer the assigned questions in the reading section of your science notebook.	❒ Take the Chapter 22 Test from *CK-12 Chemistry.*	❒ Record what you have done in the lab section of your science notebook.
Other Notes				

Week 4	Unit 4 (Survey Course)	2-Day
Weekly Topic		
➔ This week will look at electrochemistry.		
	Day 1	Day 2
Textbook	❒ Read *CK-12 Chemistry* Sections 23.1 and 23.2.	❒ Read *CK-12 Chemistry* Section 23.3.
Writing	❒ Add the vocabulary to the glossary section of your science notebook. ❒ Take the Chapter 22 Test from *CK-12 Chemistry.*	❒ Answer the assigned questions in the reading section of your science notebook.
Events in Science	❒ Choose one of the Events in Science assignments to do and add your work to the events section of your science notebook.	
Other Notes		

Week 5 Notes - Nuclear Chemistry

Textbook Assignments

Reading

📖 *CK-12 Chemistry* Sections 24.1, 24.2, 24.3

Written

After you finish reading, answer questions #3-5 in section 24.1, #1-5 in section 24.2, and #1-6 in section 24.3. File your work in the reading section of your science notebook. Then, define the following terms in the glossary section of your science notebook:

- ☐ Alpha Particle
- ☐ Band of Stability
- ☐ Mass Defect
- ☐ Nuclear Reaction
- ☐ Nuclide
- ☐ Radioisotope
- ☐ Transmutation
- ☐ Critical Mass
- ☐ Ionizing Radiation
- ☐ Rem
- ☐ Film Badge
- ☐ Radioactive Dating

Experiment - Observe Some Properties of Colloids and Suspensions

Purpose

The purpose of this lab is to observe some properties of colloids and suspensions.

Pre-Reading

Read the background and procedure sections for the "Observe Some Properties of Colloids and Suspensions" lab on pg. 166 in *The Home Scientist Chemistry Laboratory Manual.*

Procedure

✓ Do the lab entitled "Observe Some Properties of Colloids and Suspensions" on pg. 166 in *The Home Scientist Chemistry Laboratory Manual.*

Lab Notebook

Write down on a sheet of paper or type out your notes as you do the experiment. After you are done, print out your lab notes and add them to the lab section of your science notebook.

Lab Questions

Complete the multiple choice section of the "Observe Some Properties of Colloids and Suspensions" lab on pg. 168 in *The Home Scientist Chemistry Laboratory Manual.* Record the answers in the lab section of your science notebook.

Online Lab - Lab 29: Molecular Weight Determination by Acid-Base Titration

Purpose

The purpose of this online lab is to determine the molar mass of a solid acid by titration methods.

Pre-Reading

- Print and read the section of the workbook for the "Molecular Weight Determination by Acid-Base Titration" online lab.

Procedure

- ✓ Do the lab entitled "Molecular Weight Determination by Acid-Base Titration" and answer the questions as you work through the online lab.

Lab Notebook

- ☞ Add the completed workbook pages that were printed to the lab notebook.

Events in Science

Current Events

- Find a current events article relating to the field of chemistry and complete the article summary sheet found on pg. 245 of the Appendix. Once you are done, add the sheet to the events section of your science notebook.

Historical Figures

- Continue to research the life and work of Marie Curie.

Hands-on Activity

Optional Hands-on

- ✂ Observe radioactive decay with food. You will need a timer and at least thirty two bite-sized pieces of food, such as raisins, cereal puffs, or M&M's. Set out thirty-two pieces of the bite-sized food in front of you and start the timer. At 2 minutes, eat sixteen pieces. After 2 more minutes, eat eight pieces. After 2 more minutes, eat four pieces. After 2 more minutes, eat two pieces. After 2 more minutes, eat one piece. After 2 more minutes, break the one remaining piece in half and eat one of the halves. After 2 more minutes, break the one remaining piece in half and eat one of the halves. After 2 more minutes, eat any of the remaining crumbs. (*This is a simple look at how a half-life works.*)

Week 5 Supply List

Weekly Experiment	
Supplies from CK01B Chemistry Kit	❒ Goggles, Pipette, Stirring rod
Additional Supplies From Home	❒ Gloves, Butane lighter or other flame source, Dishwashing detergent or liquid soap, Drinking glasses or jars (see text), Laser pointer (optional; see text), Milk (whole or 2% homogenized), Smoke source (see text), Sodium chloride (table salt), Soft drink (e.g. club soda or 7-Up), Starch water (see text), Talcum - baby or foot powder, Vegetable oil
Hands-on Activity	
Supplies Needed	❒ Timer, 32 Bite-sized pieces of food, such as raisins, cereal puffs, or M&M's

Week 5	Unit 4 (Honors Course)				5-Day
Weekly Topic					
➔ This week will look at nuclear chemistry.					
	Day 1	Day 2	Day 3	Day 4	Day 5
Textbook and Experiment	❒ Read *CK-12 Chemistry* Sections 24.1 and 24.2.	❒ Read *CK-12 Chemistry* Section 24.3.	❒ Read the background and procedure sections for the week's lab.	❒ Do the "Observe Some Properties of Colloids and Suspensions" lab on pg. 166 in *The Home Scientist Chemistry Laboratory Manual.*	❒ Do the optional Hands-on Assignment - Nuclear Decay.
Writing	❒ Add the vocabulary to the glossary section of your science notebook.	❒ Answer the assigned questions in the reading section of your science notebook.	❒ Take the Chapter 23 Test from *CK-12 Chemistry.*	❒ Record what you have done in the lab section of your science notebook.	❒ Complete the lab review questions for the week.
Events in Science	❒ Choose one of the Events in Science assignments to do and add your work to the events section of your science notebook.				
Other Notes					

Week 5	Unit 4 (Standard Course)			4-Day
Weekly Topic				
➔ This week will look at nuclear chemistry.				
	Day 1	Day 2	Day 3	Day 4
Textbook and Experiment	❐ Read *CK-12 Chemistry* Sections 24.1 and 24.2.	❐ Read *CK-12 Chemistry* Section 24.3.	❐ Read the background and procedure sections for the week's lab.	❐ Do the "Observe Some Properties of Colloids and Suspensions" lab on pg. 166 in *The Home Scientist Chemistry Laboratory Manual.* **OR** ❐ Do the online lab "Molecular Weight Determination by Acid-Base Titration."
Writing	❐ Add the vocabulary to the glossary section of your science notebook.	❐ Answer the assigned questions in the reading section of your science notebook.	❐ Take the Chapter 23 Test from *CK-12 Chemistry.*	❐ Record what you have done in the lab section of your science notebook.
Other Notes				

Week 5	Unit 4 (Survey Course)	2-Day
Weekly Topic		
➔ This week will look at nuclear chemistry.		
	Day 1	Day 2
Textbook	❒ Read *CK-12 Chemistry* Sections 24.1 and 24.2.	❒ Read *CK-12 Chemistry* Section 24.3.
Writing	❒ Add the vocabulary to the glossary section of your science notebook. ❒ Take the Chapter 23 Test from *CK-12 Chemistry*.	❒ Answer the assigned questions in the reading section of your science notebook.
Events in Science	❒ Choose one of the Events in Science assignments to do and add your work to the events section of your science notebook.	
Other Notes		

Week 6 Notes - Organic Chemistry, part 1

Textbook Assignments

Reading

📖 *CK-12 Chemistry* Section 25.1, 25.2

Written

After you finish reading, answer questions #1-8 in section 25.1, and questions #3-6 in section 25.2, and file your work in the reading section of your science notebook. Then, define the following terms in the glossary section of your science notebook:

- ☐ Alkane
- ☐ Alkene
- ☐ Geometric Isomer
- ☐ Optical Isomer
- ☐ Cycloalkane
- ☐ Cycloalkene
- ☐ Delocalized Electrons
- ☐ Saturated Hydrocarbon
- ☐ Structural Isomer

Experiment - Determine a Reaction Order

Purpose

The purpose of this lab is to Determine a Reaction Order.

Pre-Reading

Read the background and procedure sections for the "Determine a Reaction Order" lab on pg. 100 in *The Home Scientist Chemistry Laboratory Manual.*

Procedure

✓ Do the lab entitled "Determine a Reaction Order" on pg. 100 in *The Home Scientist Chemistry Laboratory Manual.*

Lab Notebook

☞ Write down on a sheet of paper or type out your notes as you do the experiment. After you are done, print out your lab notes and add them to the lab section of your science notebook.

Lab Questions

Complete the multiple choice section of the "Determine a Reaction Order" lab on pg. 106 in *The Home Scientist Chemistry Laboratory Manual.* Record the answers in the lab section of your science notebook.

Online Lab - Lab 30: Redox Titrations - Determination of Iron

Purpose

The purpose of this online lab is to determine the weight percent of an iron compound in a sample using an oxidation-reduction titration.

Pre-Reading

Print and read the section of the workbook for the "Redox Titrations - Determination of

Iron" online lab.

Procedure

✓ Do the lab entitled "Redox Titrations - Determination of Iron" and answer the questions as you work through the online lab.

Lab Notebook

☞ Add the completed workbook pages that were printed to the lab notebook.

Events in Science

Current Events

🕒 Find a current events article relating to the field of chemistry and complete the article summary sheet found on pg. 245 of the Appendix. Once you are done, add the sheet to the events section of your science notebook.

Historical Figures

🕒 Begin to work on your paper on the life and work of Marie Curie. This week, aim to complete your outline. See pg. 14 for more directions. You will have three weeks to complete this paper.

Hands-on Activity

Optional Hands-on

✂ Make a bouncy ball polymer. You will need glue (Elmer's white or clear gel will work), food coloring, cornstarch, two small mixing cups, plastic spoon, water, and Borax. Directions can be found under #3 at the following post: https://elementalscience.com/blogs/science-activities/3-science-activities-you-can-do-with-borax.

Week 6 Supply List

Weekly Experiment	
Supplies from CK01B Chemistry Kit	❒ Goggles, Reaction plate 24-well, Pipettes, Thermometer, Hydrochloric acid 6 M, Sodium thiosulfate 1 M
Additional Supplies From Home	❒ Gloves, Desk lamp or other bright light source, Clock or watch with second hand, Toothpicks, Newspaper or other printed matter, Distilled water, Graphing paper/calculator/software
Hands-on Activity	
Supplies Needed	❒ Glue (Elmer's white or clear, gel will work), Food coloring, Cornstarch, 2 Small mixing cups, Plastic spoon, Water, Borax

Week 6	Unit 4 (Honors Course)				5-Day
Weekly Topic					
➔ This week will begin a look at organic chemistry.					
	Day 1	Day 2	Day 3	Day 4	Day 5
Textbook and Experiment	❐ Read *CK-12 Chemistry* Section 25.1.	❐ Read *CK-12 Chemistry* Section 25.2.	❐ Read the background and procedure sections for the week's lab.	❐ Do the "Determine a Reaction Order" lab on pg. 100 in *The Home Scientist Chemistry Laboratory Manual.*	❐ Do the optional Hands-on Assignment - Polymer Ball.
Writing	❐ Add the vocabulary to the glossary section of your science notebook.	❐ Answer the assigned questions in the reading section of your science notebook.	❐ Take the Chapter 24 Test from *CK-12 Chemistry.*	❐ Record what you have done in the lab section of your science notebook.	❐ Complete the lab review questions for the week.
Events in Science	❐ Choose one of the Events in Science assignments to do and add your work to the events section of your science notebook.				
Other Notes					

Week 6	Unit 4 (Standard Course)			4-Day
Weekly Topic				
➔ This week will begin a look at organic chemistry.				
	Day 1	Day 2	Day 3	Day 4
Textbook and Experiment	❐ Read *CK-12 Chemistry* Section 25.1.	❐ Read *CK-12 Chemistry* Section 25.2.	❐ Read the background and procedure sections for the week's lab.	❐ Do the "Determine a Reaction Order" lab on pg. 100 in *The Home Scientist Chemistry Laboratory Manual.* **OR** ❐ Do the online lab "Redox Titrations - Determination of Iron."
Writing	❐ Add the vocabulary to the glossary section of your science notebook.	❐ Answer the assigned questions in the reading section of your science notebook.	❐ Take the Chapter 24 Test from *CK-12 Chemistry.*	❐ Record what you have done in the lab section of your science notebook.
Other Notes				

Week 6	Unit 4 (Survey Course)	2-Day
Weekly Topic		
➔ This week will begin a look at organic chemistry.		
	Day 1	Day 2
Textbook	❒ Read *CK-12 Chemistry* Section 25.1.	❒ Read *CK-12 Chemistry* Section 25.2.
Writing	❒ Add the vocabulary to the glossary section of your science notebook. ❒ Take the Chapter 24 Test from *CK-12 Chemistry*.	❒ Answer the assigned questions in the reading section of your science notebook.
Events in Science	❒ Choose one of the Events in Science assignments to do and add your work to the events section of your science notebook.	
Other Notes		

Week 7 Notes - Organic Chemistry, part 2

Textbook Assignments

Reading

📖 *CK-12 Chemistry* Section 25.3, 25.4

Written

After you finish reading, answer questions #1-5 in section 25.3 and questions #3-6 in section 25.4, and file your work in the reading section of your science notebook. Then, define the following terms in the glossary section of your science notebook:

- ☐ Aldehyde
- ☐ Alkyl Halide
- ☐ Amine
- ☐ Ester
- ☐ Ketone
- ☐ Addition Reaction
- ☐ Esterification
- ☐ Monomer
- ☐ Saponification
- ☐ Substitution Reaction

Experiment - Determine Vitamin C Concentration in Urine

Purpose

The purpose of this lab is to explore synthesis reactions and purity of their products.

Pre-Reading

Read the background and procedure sections for the "Determine Vitamin C Concentration in Urine" lab on pg. 171 in *The Home Scientist Chemistry Laboratory Manual.*

Procedure

✓ Do the lab entitled "Determine Vitamin C Concentration in Urine" on pg. 171 in *The Home Scientist Chemistry Laboratory Manual.*

Lab Notebook

☞ Write down on a sheet of paper or type out your notes as you do the experiment. After you are done, print out your lab notes and add them to the lab section of your science notebook.

Lab Questions

Complete the multiple choice section of the "Determine Vitamin C Concentration in Urine" lab on pg. 175 in *The Home Scientist Chemistry Laboratory Manual.* Record the answers in the lab section of your science notebook.

Online Lab - Lab 24: Qualitative Analysis

Purpose

The purpose of this online lab is to use a systematic panel of chemical tests to identify up to eight metal cations in an unknown solution.

Pre-Reading

- Print and read the section of the workbook for the "Qualitative Analysis" online lab.

Procedure

- ✓ Do the lab entitled "Qualitative Analysis" and answer the questions as you work through the online lab.

Lab Notebook

- Add the completed workbook pages that were printed to the lab notebook.

Events in Science

Current Events

- Find a current events article relating to the field of chemistry and complete the article summary sheet found on pg. 245 of the Appendix. Once you are done, add the sheet to the events section of your science notebook.

Historical Figures

- Continue work on your paper on the life and work of Marie Curie. This week, aim to complete your rough draft. See pg. 14 for more directions.

Hands-on Activity

Optional Hands-on

- Use chemistry to make a work of art. You will need absorbent material (coffee filter or white cotton material both work well), rubbing alcohol (at least 80% isopropyl or above), eyedropper, coffee can (or a wide-mouthed jar or bowl), rubber band, permanent markers in a variety of colors, and newspaper. Directions for this project can be found here: https://elementalscience.com/blogs/science-activities/120199363-marker-chromatography-art.

Week 7 Supply List

Weekly Experiment	
Supplies from CK01B Chemistry Kit	❒ Goggles, Ascorbic acid tablet, Beaker 100 mL, Centrifuge tubes 15 mL, Graduated cylinder 10 mL, Iodine/iodide solution, Pipettes, Stirring rod, Test tube - glass, Test tube rack
Additional Supplies From Home	❒ Gloves, Desk lamp or other strong light source, Foam cups, Paper towel, Starch water (see text), Urine specimen(s) (see text), Vitamin C tablet(s), Water distilled
Hands-on Activity	
Supplies Needed	❒ Absorbent material (coffee filter or white cotton material both work well), Rubbing alcohol (at least 80% Isopropyl or above), Eyedropper, Coffee can (or a wide-mouthed jar or bowl), Rubber band, Permanent markers in a variety of colors, Newspaper

Week 7	Unit 4 (Honors Course)				5-Day
Weekly Topic					
➔ This week will wrap up a look at organic chemistry.					
	Day 1	Day 2	Day 3	Day 4	Day 5
Textbook and Experiment	❒ Read *CK-12 Chemistry* Section 25.3.	❒ Read *CK-12 Chemistry* Section 25.4.	❒ Read the background and procedure sections for the week's lab.	❒ Do the "Determine Vitamin C Concentration in Urine" lab on pg. 171 in *The Home Scientist Chemistry Laboratory Manual*.	❒ Do the optional Hands-on Assignment - Chemical Art.
Writing	❒ Add the vocabulary to the glossary section of your science notebook.	❒ Answer the assigned questions in the reading section of your science notebook.		❒ Record what you have done in the lab section of your science notebook.	❒ Complete the lab review questions for the week.
Events in Science	❒ Choose one of the Events in Science assignments to do and add your work to the events section of your science notebook.				
Other Notes					

Week 7	Unit 4 (Standard Course)			4-Day
Weekly Topic				
➔ This week will wrap up a look at organic chemistry.				
	Day 1	Day 2	Day 3	Day 4
Textbook and Experiment	❐ Read *CK-12 Chemistry* Section 25.3.	❐ Read *CK-12 Chemistry* Section 25.4.	❐ Read the background and procedure sections for the week's lab.	❐ Do the "Determine Vitamin C Concentration in Urine" lab on pg. 171 in *The Home Scientist Chemistry Laboratory Manual.* **OR** ❐ Do the online lab "Qualitative Analysis."
Writing	❐ Add the vocabulary to the glossary section of your science notebook.	❐ Answer the assigned questions in the reading section of your science notebook.		❐ Record what you have done in the lab section of your science notebook.
Other Notes				

Week 7	Unit 4 (Survey Course)	2-Day
Weekly Topic		
➔ This week will wrap up a look at organic chemistry.		
	Day 1	Day 2
Textbook	❒ Read *CK-12 Chemistry* Section 25.3.	❒ Read *CK-12 Chemistry* Section 25.4.
Writing	❒ Add the vocabulary to the glossary section of your science notebook.	❒ Answer the assigned questions in the reading section of your science notebook.
Events in Science	❒ Choose one of the Events in Science assignments to do and add your work to the events section of your science notebook.	
Other Notes		

Week 8 Notes - Biochemistry, part 1

Textbook Assignments

Reading

📖 *CK-12 Chemistry* Section 26.1, 26.2

Written

After you finish reading, answer questions #1-6 in section 26.1 and questions #1-7 in section 26.2, and file your work in the reading section of your science notebook. Then, define the following terms in the glossary section of your science notebook:

- ☐ Disaccharide
- ☐ Monosaccharide
- ☐ Polysaccharide
- ☐ Peptide Bond
- ☐ Polypeptide
- ☐ Quaternary Structure
- ☐ Tertiary Structure

Experiment - Detect Lead in Household Materials

Purpose

The purpose of this lab is to Detect Lead in Household Materials.

Pre-Reading

Read the background and procedure sections for the "Detect Lead in Household Materials" lab on pg. 176 in *The Home Scientist Chemistry Laboratory Manual.*

Procedure

✓ Do the lab entitled "Detect Lead in Household Materials" on pg. 176 in *The Home Scientist Chemistry Laboratory Manual.*

Lab Notebook

☞ Write down on a sheet of paper or type out your notes as you do the experiment. After you are done, print out your lab notes and add them to the lab section of your science notebook.

Lab Questions

Complete the multiple choice section of the "Detect Lead in Household Materials" lab on pg. 181 in *The Home Scientist Chemistry Laboratory Manual.* Record the answers in the lab section of your science notebook.

Online Lab - Lab 21: Electrolytes

Purpose

The purpose of this online lab is to classify compounds as electrolytes by testing their conductivity in aqueous solution.

Pre-Reading

Print and read the section of the workbook for the "Electrolytes" online lab.

Procedure

✓ Do the lab entitled "Electrolytes" and answer the questions as you work through the online lab.

Lab Notebook

☞ Add the completed workbook pages that were printed to the lab notebook.

Events in Science

Current Events

🕒 Find a current events article relating to the field of chemistry and complete the article summary sheet found on pg. 245 of the Appendix. Once you are done, add the sheet to the events section of your science notebook.

Historical Figures

🕒 Continue work on your paper on the life and work of Marie Curie. This week, aim to complete your final draft. See pg. 14 for more directions.

Hands-on Activity

Optional Hands-on

✂ Burn some sugar to make a soda snake. You will need sand, rubbing alcohol, baking soda, sugar, a heat-proof surface, a bowl, and matches. Directions for this activity can be found here: http://www.anordinarylife.co.uk/2012/05/experiment-soda-snake.html?m=1.

Week 8 Supply List

Weekly Experiment	
Supplies from CK01B Chemistry Kit	❒ Goggles, Centrifuge tube(s) 15 mL and/or 50 mL, Graduated cylinder 10 mL, Lead(II) acetate, Pipettes, Potassium dichromate, Potassium iodide, Reaction plate 24-well, Sharpie marking pen, Sodium sulfide
Additional Supplies From Home	❒ Gloves, Desk lamp or other strong light source, Knife, Paper towels, Specimens (see text), Vinegar - distilled white, Water distilled
Hands-on Activity	
Supplies Needed	❒ Sand, Rubbing alcohol, Baking soda, Sugar, Heat proof surface, Bowl, Matches

Week 8	Unit 4 (Honors Course)				5-Day
Weekly Topic					
➔ This week will begin a look at biochemistry.					
	Day 1	Day 2	Day 3	Day 4	Day 5
Textbook and Experiment	❒ Read *CK-12 Chemistry* Section 26.1.	❒ Read *CK-12 Chemistry* Section 26.2.	❒ Read the background and procedure sections for the week's lab.	❒ Do the "Detect Lead in Household Materials" lab on pg. 176 in *The Home Scientist Chemistry Laboratory Manual.*	❒ Do the optional Hands-on Assignment - Soda Snake.
Writing	❒ Add the vocabulary to the glossary section of your science notebook.	❒ Answer the assigned questions in the reading section of your science notebook.	❒ Take the Chapter 25 Test from *CK-12 Chemistry.*	❒ Record what you have done in the lab section of your science notebook.	❒ Complete the lab review questions for the week.
Events in Science	❒ Choose one of the Events in Science assignments to do and add your work to the events section of your science notebook.				
Other Notes					

Week 8	Unit 4 (Standard Course)			4-Day
Weekly Topic				
➔ This week will begin a look at biochemistry.				
	Day 1	Day 2	Day 3	Day 4
Textbook and Experiment	❒ Read *CK-12 Chemistry* Section 26.1.	❒ Read *CK-12 Chemistry* Section 26.2.	❒ Read the background and procedure sections for the week's lab.	❒ Do the "Detect Lead in Household Materials" lab on pg. 176 in *The Home Scientist Chemistry Laboratory Manual.* **OR** ❒ Do the online lab "Electrolytes."
Writing	❒ Add the vocabulary to the glossary section of your science notebook.	❒ Answer the assigned questions in the reading section of your science notebook.	❒ Take the Chapter 25 Test from *CK-12 Chemistry.*	❒ Record what you have done in the lab section of your science notebook.
Other Notes				

Week 8	Unit 4 (Survey Course)	2-Day
Weekly Topic		
➔ This week will begin a look at biochemistry.		
	Day 1	Day 2
Textbook	❒ Read *CK-12 Chemistry* Section 26.1.	❒ Read *CK-12 Chemistry* Section 26.2.
Writing	❒ Add the vocabulary to the glossary section of your science notebook. ❒ Take the Chapter 25 Test from *CK-12 Chemistry.*	❒ Answer the assigned questions in the reading section of your science notebook.
Events in Science	❒ Choose one of the Events in Science assignments to do and add your work to the events section of your science notebook.	
Other Notes		

Week 9 Notes - Biochemistry, part 2

Textbook Assignments

Reading

📖 *CK-12 Chemistry* Section 26.3, 26.4

Written

After you finish reading, answer questions #4-8 in section 26.3 and questions #5-8 in section 26.4, and file your work in the reading section of your science notebook. Then, define the following terms in the glossary section of your science notebook:

- ☐ Lipid
- ☐ Triglyceride
- ☐ Saturated Fat
- ☐ Phospholipid
- ☐ Nucleic Acid
- ☐ Nucleotide

Experiment

☞ There is no experiment scheduled for this week.

Online Lab

☞ There is no online lab scheduled for this week.

Events in Science

Current Events

🕒 There is no assignment for this week.

Historical Figures

🕒 There is no assignment for this week.

Hands-on Activity

Optional Hands-on

✂ Extract DNA from a piece of fruit. You will need sliced fruit (a banana, strawberry, kiwi, or tomato will all work), dish soap, salt, ice-cold isopropyl alcohol (70% or higher), zipper-style plastic bag, coffee filter, funnel, wooden coffee stirrer, and a test tube or clear glass. You can find the directions for this activity here: http://sassafrasscience.com/extracting-dna-uncle-cecil/.

Week 9 Supply List

Weekly Experiment	
Supplies from CK01B Chemistry Kit	❒ None
Additional Supplies From Home	❒ None
Hands-on Activity	
Supplies Needed	❒ Sliced fruit (a banana, strawberry, kiwi, or tomato will all work), Dish soap, Salt, Ice-cold Isopropyl alcohol (70% or higher), Zipper-style plastic bag, Coffee filter, Funnel, Wooden coffee stirrer, Test tube (or clear glass)

Week 9	Unit 4 (Honors Course)				5-Day
Weekly Topic					
➔ This week will wrap up a look at biochemistry.					
	Day 1	Day 2	Day 3	Day 4	Day 5
Textbook and Experiment	❒ Read *CK-12 Chemistry* Section 26.3.	❒ Read *CK-12 Chemistry* Section 26.4.	❒ Take the Chapter 26 Test from *CK-12 Chemistry*.	❒ Do the optional Hands-on Assignment - DNA Extraction.	
Writing	❒ Add the vocabulary to the glossary section of your science notebook.	❒ Answer the assigned questions in the reading section of your science notebook.			
Other Notes					

Week 9	Unit 4 (Standard Course)			4-Day
Weekly Topic				
➔ This week will wrap up a look at biochemistry.				
	Day 1	Day 2	Day 3	Day 4
Textbook and Experiment	❒ Read *CK-12 Chemistry* Section 26.3.	❒ Read *CK-12 Chemistry* Section 26.4.	❒ Take the Chapter 26 Test from *CK-12 Chemistry.*	
Writing	❒ Add the vocabulary to the glossary section of your science notebook.	❒ Answer the assigned questions in the reading section of your science notebook.		
Other Notes				

Week 9	Unit 4 (Survey Course)	2-Day
Weekly Topic		
➔ This week will wrap up a look at biochemistry.		
	Day 1	Day 2
Textbook	❒ Read *CK-12 Chemistry* Sections 26.3 and 26.4.	❒ Take the Chapter 26 Test from *CK-12 Chemistry*.
Writing	❒ Add the vocabulary to the glossary section of your science notebook.	❒ Answer the assigned questions in the reading section of your science notebook.
Other Notes		

Chemistry for High School

Appendix

Additional Supplies from Home Master Supply List

Unit 1: Introduction to Chemistry

Week	Supplies Needed
1	*No additional supplies needed*
2	Gloves, Balance (optional), Microwave oven, Oven - baking dish, Refrigerator/ freezer, Measuring spoons (optional), Soda bottle- pint/500 mL (empty and clean), Storage container (wide mouth, with lid), Sodium bicarbonate (baking soda), Distilled water
3	Gloves, Digital multimeter (DMM) with probes, Microwave oven, Paper towels, Soda bottle (clean and dry), Sucrose (table sugar), Distilled water
4	Gloves, Balance (optional), Foam cups (or similar containers), Freezer, Measuring spoons (if no balance), Sodium chloride (table salt), Sucrose (table sugar), Distilled water, Ice (crushed or chipped)
5	Gloves, Microwave oven, Refrigerator, Soda bottles (empty), Watch or clock with second hand, Distilled white vinegar (supermarket), Graphing paper/calculator/ software
6	Gloves, Microwave oven, Oven mitts or tongs, Paper (sheet of copy paper or similar), Paper towels, Refrigerator/freezer, Tablespoon (measuring or standard), Teaspoon (measuring or standard), Sodium bicarbonate (baking soda), Sodium chloride (table salt)
7	Gloves, Cotton swabs, Pencil, Hair dryer (optional), Paper towels, Scissors, Toothpicks-plastic, Transparent tape, Additional felt-tip pens (optional), Isopropyl alcohol (70%, 91%, or 99%)
8	*No additional supplies needed.*
9	*No additional supplies needed.*

Unit 2: Bonding and Reactions

Week	Supplies Needed
1	Gloves, Butane lighter (or other flame source), Sheet of white paper
2	Gloves, Butane lighter (or other flame source), Sodium bicarbonate (baking soda)
3	Gloves, Butane lighter (or other flame source), Rubber band, Digital multimeter (optional), Water-distilled
4	Gloves, Microwave oven, Sodium chloride (table salt), Water-distilled
5	Gloves, Paper-white
6	Gloves, Desk lamp or other strong light source, Sheets of white and black paper, Distilled water
7	Gloves, Distilled water
8	Gloves, Soda bottle (2-liter, clean and empty), Vegetable oil
9	Gloves, Freezer, Microwave oven, Ice, Vegetable oil

Unit 3: Water and Equilibrium

Week	Supplies Needed
1	Gloves, Scissors, Toothpicks plastic, Water (distilled)
2	Gloves, Desk lamp or other strong light source, Paper or cloth (black), Water (distilled)
3	Gloves, Balance (optional), Foam cup (with lid), Soda bottle 2-liter (empty), Sodium chloride (table salt)
4	Gloves, Aluminum foil, Digital multimeter (DMM), Knife, Lemon
5	Gloves, Balance (optional), Foam cups (with lid), Ice
6	Gloves, Balance (optional), Foam cup (with lid), Microwave oven, Paper towels, US cent coins
7	Gloves, Foam cup (with lid)
8	*No additional supplies needed.*

Unit 4: Organic Chemistry and More

Week	Supplies Needed
1	Gloves, Household materials to test (see text), Scissors, Distilled water
2	Gloves, Desk lamp (or other strong light source), Distilled water, Paper, Vinegar-distilled white
3	Gloves, Desk lamp or other strong light source, Sheet of white paper, Toothpicks, Distilled water
4	Gloves, Aluminum foil, Desk lamp or other incandescent light, Fluorescent light source, Foam cups, Paper (white copy or similar), Water-distilled, Watch or clock
5	Gloves, Butane lighter or other flame source, Dishwashing detergent or liquid soap, Drinking glasses or jars (see text), Laser pointer (optional; see text), Milk (whole or 2% homogenized), Smoke source (see text), Sodium chloride (table salt), Soft drink (e.g. club soda or 7-Up), Starch water (see text), Talcum - baby or foot powder, Vegetable oil
6	Gloves, Desk lamp or other bright light source, Clock or watch with second hand, Toothpicks, Newspaper or other printed matter, Distilled water, Graphing paper/calculator/software
7	Gloves, Desk lamp or other strong light source, Foam cups, Paper towel, Starch water (see text), Urine specimen(s) (see text), Vitamin C tablet(s), Water distilled
8	Gloves, Desk lamp or other strong light source, Knife, Paper towels, Specimens (see text), Vinegar - distilled white, Water distilled
9	*No additional supplies needed.*

Hands-on Activities Master Supply List

Unit 1: Introduction to Chemistry

Week	Supplies Needed
1	Heavy cream, Milk, Sugar, Vanilla, 1 Quart size ziploc plastic bag, Crushed ice, 1 Gallon size ziploc plastic bag, Rock salt
2	Cup, Ice cubes, Pot, Thermometer
3	*No supplies needed.*
4	Honey, Karo syrup, Liquid dish soap, Water, Vegetable oil, Rubbing alcohol, Lamp oil, Glass jar
5	Blue, brown, and red colored beads or mini-M&M's (at least 30 of each), *Atoms and Isotopes* game board and cards
6	4 Pipe cleaners, 9 Round beads in three different colors (3 of each color)
7	6 Small balloons, Tape
8	*No supplies needed.*
9	Sample liquids (oil, fruit juice, water, saltwater, and so on), Ice cube tray, Instant thermometer

Unit 2: Bonding and Reactions

Week	Supplies Needed
1	Cake frosting, Red and yellow bite-sized candies
2	Cake frosting, Red and yellow bite-sized candies
3	Supplies will vary based on the activities you choose to do.
4	Baking soda, White vinegar, Cup
5	*No supplies needed.*
6	Penny, Water, Eye dropper
7	Dry ice, Cup, Water, Dish soap, 2 Plates
8	Medicine dropper, 2 Mini-marshmallows
9	Sample liquids (oil, fruit juice, water, saltwater, and so on), Ice cube tray, Instant thermometer

Unit 3: Water and Equilibrium

Week	Supplies Needed
1	Ziploc baggie, Vinegar, Baking soda, Paper towel, Scale
2	Glass jar, Pipe cleaner, String, Pencil, Water, Borax
3	3 Cups, Water, Food coloring, Salt, Instant-read thermometer
4	Water, Food coloring, 3 Clear cups

5	Epsom salts, Water, Cup, Instant-read thermometer
6	Hydrogen peroxide, Dish soap, Yeast, Water, Bottle, Cup
7	*No supplies needed.*
8	Balloon, Scissors

Unit 4: Organic Chemistry and More

Week	Supplies Needed
1	Head a red cabbage, Variety of items from your kitchen to test (such as lemon juice, baking soda, soda, or detergent)
2	White vinegar, Ammonia, Water, Cabbage juice indicator, (*from week 1*) Eyedropper, Cup
3	Piece of silver, Aluminum foil, Heat-resistant container, Hot water, Baking soda, Salt
4	LED bulb, 4 Lemons (fresh and juicy), 4 Clean pennies, 4 Galvanized nails, 5 Alligator clips, Wire
5	Timer, 32 Bite-sized pieces of food, such as raisins, cereal puffs, or M&M's
6	Glue (Elmer's white or clear, gel will work), Food coloring, Cornstarch, 2 Small mixing cups, Plastic spoon, Water, Borax
7	Absorbent material (coffee filter or white cotton material both work well), Rubbing alcohol (at least 80% Isopropyl or above), Eyedropper, Coffee can (or a wide-mouthed jar or bowl), Rubber band, Permanent markers in a variety of colors, Newspaper
8	Sand, Rubbing alcohol, Baking soda, Sugar, Heat proof surface, Bowl, Matches
9	Sliced fruit (a banana, strawberry, kiwi, or tomato will all work), Dish soap, Salt, Ice-cold Isopropyl alcohol (70% or higher), Zipper-style plastic bag, Coffee filter, Funnel, Wooden coffee stirrer, Test tube (or clear glass)

Scientist Biography Report Grading Rubric

Spelling (points x 1)

4 points: No spelling mistakes.

3 points: 1-2 spelling mistakes and not distracting to the reader.

2 points: 3-4 spelling mistakes and somewhat distracting.

1 point: 5 spelling mistakes and somewhat distracting.

0 points: > 5 spelling mistakes and no proofreading obvious.

Points Earned __________

Grammar (points x 1)

4 points: No grammatical mistakes.

3 points: 1-2 grammatical mistakes and not distracting to the reader.

2 points: 3-4 grammatical mistakes and somewhat distracting.

1 point: 5 grammatical mistakes and somewhat distracting.

0 points: > 5 grammatical mistakes and no proofreading obvious.

Points Earned __________

Introduction to the Scientist (points x 2)

4 points: Includes thorough summary of the scientist's biographical information and why the student chose the particular scientist.

3 points: Adequate summary of the scientist's biographical information and why the student chose the particular scientist.

2 points: Inaccurate or incomplete summary of one of the scientist's biographical information and why the student chose the particular scientist.

1 point: Inaccurate or incomplete summary of both of the scientist's biographical information and why the student chose the particular scientist.

0 points: No introduction

Points Earned __________

Description of the Scientist's Education (points x 2)

4 points: Includes thorough summary of the scientist's education.

3 points: Adequate summary of the scientist's education.

2 points: Inaccurate or incomplete summary of one of the scientist's education.

1 point: Inaccurate or incomplete summary of both of the scientist's education.

0 points: No description of the scientist's education.

Points Earned __________

Description of the Scientist's Major Contributions (points x 2)

4 points: Includes thorough summary of the scientist's major contributions.

3 points: Adequate summary of the scientist's major contributions.

2 points: Inaccurate or incomplete summary of the scientist's major contributions.

1 point: Inaccurate and incomplete summary of the scientist's major contributions.

0 points: No description of the scientist's major contributions and interesting facts of their life.

Points Earned __________

Conclusion (points x 2)

4 points: Explanation of why the student feels one should study the scientist and a summary statement about the scientist.

3 points: Adequate explanation of why the student feels one should study the scientist and a summary statement about the scientist.

2 points: Incomplete or incorrect explanation of why the student feels one should study the scientist and a summary statement about the scientist.

1 point: Conclusion does not have an explanation of why the student feels one should study the scientist and a summary statement about the scientist.

0 points: No conclusion.

Points Earned __________

Final Score = (Total Points/40) x 100%

Total Points Earned ______________

Final Score ______________

Science in the News

Date: ______________________

Headline: ______________________

____

Authored by: ______________________

My Summary: ______________________

My Thoughts: ______________________

67023376R00135

Made in the USA
Columbia, SC
24 July 2019

The MAILBOX®
The Education Center®
TEC61067
Fascinating Facts
SOCIAL STUDIES
100 Comprehension-Building Activities
grades 4–5
Harned
PARENT TEACHER STORE
$15.95
BK-FASCINATING FFCT SS4-
TEC61067
59008 20025
Fun social studies facts
Integrate social studies and reading
Nonfiction practice
Benjamin Franklin
Man of Many Talents
Ben Franklin never made money from his inventions.
Ben Franklin lived in Philadelphia for many years. He did many things to make the city better. He started a public library. He also started a volunteer fire department. Ben saw that the city streets were dirty, dark, and unpaved. He worked hard to get the streets paved and lighted.
Ben liked to create things. He invented an electric battery, a lightning rod, and bifocal glasses. Bifocal glasses have lenses with two parts in the same frame. They allow people to see near and far. These glasses are still used today. Ben also designed the Franklin stove. It kept a room warmer than a fireplace. It helped people save money because it used less fuel. Many people used the stove to heat their homes.
Ben never used any of his ideas or designs for profit. He wanted all people to be able to use them to make their lives better.
Circle the letter of the best answer.
1. Benjamin Franklin lived in ________. a. Newport b. Philadelphia
2. Which of these did Ben not do to improve his city? a. start a volunteer fire department b. start a library
3. Ben invented a ________. a. lightning rod b. electricity
4. Which of these did the Franklin stove not do? b. use less fuel c. heat a room better
5. Which of these would be a good title for this story? "A Generous Friend" b. "The Franklin Stove" c. "Helping Others"
Use the code below to reveal some of Franklin's most famous pro
Code
Poor Richard's, 1733
AN
Almanack

About This Book

Integrating social studies and reading just got easier with *Fascinating Facts: Social Studies*! The creative reproducibles in this practical resource provide **nonfiction comprehension** practice on **key social studies topics** covered in the grades 4–5 curriculum.

This easy-to-use collection features 100 reproducibles arranged in pairs. The first reproducible in each pair begins with a social studies–related fact followed by a nonfiction reading selection and comprehension activity. The second reproducible features a second activity related to what the student has read and an optional bonus activity. Complete answer keys are also included. For added fun, you'll also find a ready-to-use trivia game for whole-class or small-group review.

Help your students master key social studies concepts as they improve their reading skills with *Fascinating Facts: Social Studies* today.